Ghosts in American Houses

Also by James Reynolds

Ghosts
in American Houses

JAMES REYNOLDS

BONANZA BOOKS • NEW YORK

To
JOHN LINDQUIST

Whose immense interest in ghostly lore indicative of
the American scene has greatly aided me in compiling
the stories for this book

Contents

vii

LIST OF COLOR ILLUSTRATIONS

Introduction

ONE spring morning several years ago I started out from North Cliff Farm in Virginia on an adventure that had long been prodding my mind. I planned to spend the better part of a year motoring the length and breadth of the country, painting a series of canvasses. I wished to document the American scene, emphasizing particularly the architecture of the various regions, from the sturdy efforts of the colonizers through what is loosely termed New England Saltbox, Boston Brick, Southern Colonial, Bayou Plantation, Georgian and Federal, to Greek Revival and Hudson River Bracketed, the latter the last gasping breath of Victorian Style. As I wandered from Pennsylvania to Louisiana, from Arkansas to California, crosshatching the continent until I had painted in every state of the union, I came to realize that not only houses but barns—spacious, beguiling barns—were part of the American panorama. The barn is to the homestead what the kitchen is to the home: the heart of everyday living; simple, useful, colorful. And sometimes it is the center of death and the supernatural.

One cannot properly paint barns and living places—mountain shacks, plantation estates, townhouses, the gaudy excesses of the Far West—without learning of the people who lived in those houses. One learns of the people who lived in them, and often as not of the ghosts who still inhabit them. I was told hundreds of ghost stories, tales of endless variety, some not suitable for brush or pen, and as the weeks passed I realized I was becoming intimately acquainted with an American tradition and folklore of tremendous vitality and importance. This is word-of-mouth history; legend rather than history. Is it the lesser for being legend?

I think not. "To know the history of a country you must know its legend," said Oliver St. John Gogarty when reviewing my *Ghosts in Irish Houses*. How persistently the ghost theme occurs in our legends, and how often the supernatural provides a disturbing footnote to stories of violent death!

Writers of popular fiction usually tell of ghosts among proud old families who have descended into degeneracy, and it is true that I have recorded here accounts of questionable occurrences in "very correct" old New York and gilded, socially conscious Knob Hill, in San Francisco, but there is also Raike Gaston, spawned by a prostitute and a river gambler, with violence and lust written in his future. I have carefully pieced together the tale of a harpy begotten in Hungary who found her way to Natchez-under-the-Hill, the "anteroom of hell," and the story, infinitely poignant, of star-crossed lovers from an Ohio Valley farm, where the ghost of the girl still walks, her presence always detected first by the fragrance of white lilacs on the breeze. Here too you will meet pious Samantha Randall of Cherry Valley, New York, who loved her silver-gray barn more than her son; you will understand why when you read her story. Bella Rawhide and Timber Kate left a trail of broken heads and empty bottles from Spokane to Santa Fe; they are remembered with awe, if not with affection. For the truth is that the "birthing" of America, by and large, was both courageous and disreputable; men beyond the law pushed back the wilderness, and brought their own kind of women with them.

Persons frequently ask me, "Mr. Reynolds, have *you* ever seen a ghost?" The answer is: "Hundreds of ghosts, all over the world." More than a century ago, four men were strung from the crossbeam of an old barn at Waterford, Vermont. They are still there. Believe me or not—it is as you choose—I saw their figures silhouetted in the moonlight *before* ever I heard the story of frenzy that led to their hanging by a half-witted youth.

And so in this book, in word and picture, I present a kind of panorama of the disparate personalities whose perturbed shades still bulk large in ghostly legends of the American scene.

JAMES REYNOLDS

November 1, 1954
Fairfax
White Pine
Tennessee

Ghosts in American Houses

Ostrich Plumes on Sunday Gingham During the Week

VINCENTOWN, NEW JERSEY, 1890

A CHANCE VISITOR walking along a shaded street on the outskirts of the rambling village of Vincentown, in the heart of the cranberry-bog country of southern New Jersey, might wonder why a big, plain-faced wooden house of rather imposing size, standing well back from the street in a wilderness of tangled shrubbery and rank grass, is so neglected. Foursquare it looms, built of clapboard, now aged and silvery, warped and rimed with moss and mold. Four tall brick chimneys dominate the gabled roof.

And well might the passerby wonder. For neglected almost to the point of ruin is the "old Lawson place," as Vincentowners refer to the house when they discuss it. And discuss it they do, frequently. Strangely upsetting, eerie happenings often take place within the dry-rotted walls of this deserted house; lights move past grimy attic windows at dusk, and, often down the years since the tragedy took place, shrill, horror-sharp cries for help shatter the winter's night.

One evening many years ago, at the end of a deceptively quiet day, old Ezra Colby, handyman at the Lawson place, was finishing up his chores. He straightened his back, rubbed his rough oak-brown hands along the stringy muscles of his lean hips, and said to himself, "Do beat all how tired I git these days. Tired and lame." Standing straight, he looked down the twilight-shadowed garden. He had

3

just routed up the last of the big onions—a three-peck basket of juicy yellow bulbs —to put in the root cellar. "Gittin' plaguy dark, too," he muttered. "I better feed the old mare and git off home to my supper."

Ezra shuffled over to a tool house near some pear trees, took a lantern down from its nail, and lighted it. The dusty glass cast only a feeble light, but enough for him to see to feed Sairy, the mare. "Most over yer use, Sairy. Don't nobody care nothin' about ye but me," he said. The rheumy-eyed old horse nickered, rubbing her whiskered muzzle along Ezra's sleeve.

By now, it was nearly dark. Mid-October, but mild weather. Ezra looked up into the heavens. "Bright night. Lots o' stars." He shut the barn door and started to leave by the side gate. As he passed the bay window of the dining room, Ezra noticed that the heavy plush curtains were only half drawn. He stopped, "Never seen no light in this house before," he murmured. "Dark as tophet usually." He looked closer, "Even the window's open a mite. Warm night. Guess Mrs. Alta feels close." He was about to go on when he heard the sharp slap of a hand striking flesh smartly. He stepped onto the stone curbing under the window to see better.

Ezra stood rooted to the spot, holding his breath. Seated at the table, which lay in a pool of light from a hanging oil lamp, were three people—a man and two women. All three Ezra had seen often during the years he had worked there. But tonight they seemed somehow different. The older of the two women, Alta Lawson, and the man, Lambert, her son, were deadly quiet, watching the younger woman, Sophie, wife to Lambert. Alta, heavy-set and browned by sun and time, paid Ezra regularly but never said two words of conversation beyond giving him orders. Lambert was always drunk; most of the time, Ezra knew, he lay on a couch, sleeping or singing crazily to himself. For Sophie, the only friendly one of the trio, Ezra felt great pity. Now she was holding her face where she had been struck. Sobbing wildly, she started to rise from the table.

"Sit down!" yelled her husband. He stretched across the table and grabbed one of her arms in a drunken grip. "You hid that bottle, I tell you! I caught you at it. If I catch you again, I'll kill you, so help me! I ought to have done it years ago."

Sophie wrenched her arm free, and Ezra saw her fall across the table, a thin, faded, but still youthful figure, beating the board feebly with clenched fists.

Ezra shifted his gaze to Alta, at the head of the table. She sat glowering, her chin sunk on her folded arms. Ezra blinked. The last time he had seen Alta Lawson, in the garden just before dark, she had worn a stained gingham dress, as she always did when she worked around the place. Now her hair was piled up, with ribbons in it. She was dressed in dark-red velvet, with shiny objects around the neck and sleeves. Lambert wore a dark jacket. His soiled white shirt was pulled open at the neck. Sophie Lawson still wore the dingy, apron-covered print dress she had worked in all afternoon.

Even to Ezra, who had never been farther afield than Burlington, this was a strange picture—the hysterical woman, the drink-wracked man, and the silent, somber watcher at the end of the table. Ezra rubbed his chin. "It ain't right. It's bad, somehow," he whispered to himself. Suddenly the picture, so like a tableau of hate, changed. Words from Alta Lawson's lips sped like sharp flints at Sophie.

"Get upstairs with your sniveling. I can't stand any more of you."

Lambert leaned across the table, shouting, "Get out! Go on! One day I'll get so mad I'll kill you for sure! Get out!"

Stumbling blindly, Sophie ran from the room. The sound of her footsteps on the bare stairboards diminished into silence. Ezra continued to watch, fascinated.

Alta sat back in her chair, regarding Lambert with a sneer. For a long time, the contemptuous eyes of the mother held the red-rimmed, furtive ones of her son, the son whom she had planned years before to make into a rich, powerful man. Then she spat out, "You drunken weakling! You sicken me! You and Sophie are two of a kind. Weak as water. I hate you both." She reached under the table and hoisted a basket onto her lap. From this, she drew a bottle of the moonshine liquor made by outlaws deep in the cranberry bogs. As Lambert watched, his mother again caught and held his eyes in a basilisk stare. Slowly she slid the bottle along the table toward him. He grabbed it feverishly, pulling out the cork with his teeth.

Ezra Colby had seen enough. He went down the path and on into the main street of the village. "Feel like I been hit a wallop on the head," he mumbled to himself.

What a terrible life for the three people shut up behind the curtains of that drafty old barn of a house! Looking down the street of Vincentown, where he had been born and had lived all his life, Ezra smiled with relief. Red or white clapboard houses lined both sides of the street. No curtained windows here. Nothing to hide, he guessed. Light streamed out on the grass lawns. Everybody at supper now. Thinking of it made his mouth water. He hoped his wife would have creamed chipped beef and corn bread tonight, or fried pork and apple rings. He liked them both.

Ezra opened the gate to his front yard, and paused. His thoughts went back to the hateful scene at the Lawsons'. In a corner of his mind stirred a memory— Alta Lawson's hair. She always worked around the place wearing an old straw hat; from under the brim, hair hung to her shoulders, gray and stringy. Tonight, dressed in her finery, her hair was combed high, curled, jet black, and glossy.

"Now, how can that be?" Ezra said to himself. "A wig, maybe?" And he fell to wondering on the vanity of women and if Alta Lawson had once been handsome. Amos Lawson, he who had been Alta's husband, could have answered that question. Until Amos met Alta, he had never seen her equal.

When Amos Lawson was thirty years old, his father, Benkhard Lawson, died. He left the Lawson Ironmongery and Shipwright Enterprises, the latter at Wilmington, Delaware, to his only son, Amos. Marriageable girls for miles around preened themselves and cast bold glances in Amos Lawson's direction whenever they encountered him. Even some of the touted belles of Wilmington, Baltimore, and cities as far off as Philadelphia fluttered a bit in anticipation. Amos was tall, well-built, and had a soft-spoken way with him. His appearance was clean-cut, perhaps, rather than handsome, and, of course, he was, for the year 1840, vastly rich, and would be richer.

For a few years after his father's death, Amos kept his attention fixed on affairs at his foundry. The Burlington enterprises waxed immensely prosperous, particularly those involving stoves and ornamental ironwork. Many of the exuberant iron balconies and verandah railings, the entertaining garden fences emulating a Virginia cornfield in full stand or breaking waves on a shell-strewn beach, that one sees in Charleston, Savannah, and New Orleans were forged at the Lawson Works.

Twice a year, Amos asked his Aunt Aurelia Reedy, of Philadelphia, to act as hostess at a ball he gave at his Burlington house. He was shy and had little interest in women, though he was always agreeable to any he met. His business enterprises, the iron works and the shipyards, occupied all his time.

Then, one day, he met Alta Cossart, a beautiful girl in her early twenties, who was delivering a lunch basket to her father, a foreman at the Works. From Alta's point of view, it was a heaven-sent meeting. For Amos, had he only known it, the meeting was a most horrendous one. Alta's dossier up to this time showed her as more silly and simpering than cruel, vicious, and inordinately selfish, as she ultimately became. It is, indeed, quite easy to believe that when Saint Peter turned the last page of Alta's file, he shuddered as with an ague.

The family of Cossart—father, mother, two sons, and a daughter—had arrived in Burlington from the Channel Island of Jersey ten years before the meeting with Amos occurred. Both parents were of French-English stock, and the daughter veered definitely toward the Gallic. In her frenzied moods of jealousy, and anger over a fancied slight or a refusal of her wishes, she was wholly French. To young swains of Vincentown attempting to pay court to Alta, it soon became painfully evident that the pink-cheeked, chestnut-haired spitfire was too much of an armful for comfort. She was determined always to be on the winning side and so became a proficient cheat at games; if she could not win, she raged. One by one, the town boys, disconcerted, left her alone.

About the time the young men of Burlington gave up sparking Alta Cossart, she had her twenty-fourth birthday. This day, in May, fell on the same one that marked the annual Methodist Ladies' Sewing Circle Social Supper, only a few weeks after Amos had first become aware of her.

So Amos proposed marriage to Alta as the two were walking back to her father's small white house after the church supper. In a faltering voice, feeling greatly daring, this shy, rather diffident man, approaching middle age, offered the town beauty his heart and all his worldly possessions. Alta smiled coyly, shrugged her heliotrope-silk-clad shoulders, touched the velvet ribbons that tied her green flowered straw bonnet, and said a breathless "yes."

Odd, as one thinks of it, how one short word uttered by a pretty woman can condemn a man to a life of utter misery and he never for an instant suspect or sense impending disaster. But Amos Lawson was dazed that spring night under the New Jersey stars and the gods were not with him.

That even a grain of affection for Amos entered the heart of Alta that night or ever is scarcely possible in view of the spiteful treatment she meted out to him during the ensuing years of their ill-starred marriage. Her reasoning was plain. Amos Lawson was decidedly worth her while. He would be easy to handle and would give her a soft, luxurious life for the asking—if not for the asking, then she would get it by the taking. Alta's destiny, as she saw it, beckoned her. She was ready and able to meet it, full-square.

The wedding was held in mid-June, under a marquee on the lawn of the Methodist Church. Alta, resplendent in white muslin and lace, took the eye of all present.

Atlantic City, New York, Philadelphia—there to visit Amos's relations, the Bosworths and the Reedys—and then White Sulphur Springs, in the mountains of Virginia, were visited by the bridal couple. The bride, meanwhile, watched every move made by the fashionably dressed women she saw at the hotels where they stayed. Carefully she observed just how these ladies walked, at just what angle the tiny black-and-white lace parasols were tilted and manipulated during animated conversations, particularly with males. A really accomplished woman, she had heard, could add subtle innuendoes to her conversation by the tilt of her parasol, the way Spanish women convey all manner of meanings they dare not whisper by the flick of a fan. Alta remarked intently the exact height to lift the hoop when sitting down. This maneuver was full of pitfalls. The wide-spreading circles of wire taped together into a bell shape could betray a woman in the most embarrassing manner by kiting up over her face and displaying all her undergarments.

Until Alta's trousseau had been assembled by a dressmaker from Trenton, she had never worn a hoop. This gracefully swaying fashion had only just been taken up in America. Stories were told by returning European travelers of how Eugenie, the lovely Spanish-born Empress of France, had sponsored the hoop and originated a new manner of walking. One must seem to glide across a surface, the hoop swaying in rhythm. It took practice. Very well, Alta Lawson would glide with the best.

After lunch one day on their wedding trip, Amos said to his bride, "I am proud as proud can be, Alta, to see how all the men and women follow you with their eyes. You are the prettiest woman here, by a long shot. And you wear your clothes with such style."

Alta smiled at her husband, lowering her long lashes. She still aimed to please him; it was early yet.

"Oh, Amos, do you really think so?" She bent a little farther from the waist and adjusted her coral silk parasol at a fashionable angle. "You just wait until we get to Europe. Paris particularly. Then I'll get some real clothes. These will do for now. Nobody here knows the latest fashions. Why, just yesterday I overheard Mrs. Lamont tell another lady that she would never come here again. Too provincial. I found out from the clerk what that means. Countrified." Alta laughed boisterously. "Hayseeds, hicks. No, Paris for me."

Amos did not quite know why, but he was disturbed by this remark. He was a countryman, and proud of it. Paris held no charms for him.

Soon afterward, on the verandah of the hotel at the Springs, Alta made bold to ask Mrs. MacMasters, a decidedly frigid dowager, who her dressmaker was. All four of the dowager's chins rose at an angle. Arrogantly regarding Mrs. Lawson through her amber lorgnette, she replied; "I do not know what you mean. I am dressed by my mantuamaker."

Immediately after the Lawsons returned to Burlington from their wedding trip, Alta took a firm grasp on the tiller of the Lawson Iron Works. She never relinquished it again, as long as there was a tiller to grasp. And let you believe that no hornyhanded old navigator out of Gloucester or the seaports of Maine ever chartered a course more determinedly.

Alta was exceedingly shrewd; among other things, she believed in the element of surprise to baffle an opponent. One morning, she arrived at the office of the Lawson Iron Works with a clerk of ratings, as a chartered accountant was called in 1850. Mrs. Lawson wanted to know to a jot and tittle just how much money was in the till and what were the prospects of more, for she was going to need a prodigious lot of money to carry out her plans. Amos, bewildered, remonstrated with his wife for her highhandedness in a business that was not her concern, but to no avail. The new Mrs. Lawson scourged him with a tongue barbed with sarcasm. Generations of French ancestors rose up in her to lend added cruelty to her tirade.

"Don't you dare tell me what I can or cannot do. I'll handle this business as I see fit. You're in a rut, trying to keep it just the way your miserly old father ran it. I've heard about that. Well, let me tell you, I'll expand this works until we'll be millionaires. Do you hear that? Did you ever see a snake shed his old skin and start all fresh? Well, you're the snake, Amos. From today on, you'll have a new skin. I'll see to that. Now, shut up and get out of my light. Come on, clerk, give me those figures. Pay no attention to him."

Thus made aware of the true caliber of the seemingly docile woman he had married, Amos retired from the field, his heart and spirit broken. Soon afterward he departed for Vincentown to live in a cottage, at the edge of the village, left him by his grandmother. As a small boy, he had spent many summers with his Grandmother Reedy in the cottage, which stood almost hidden in hopvines and purple clematis, near a grove of locusts. The boy had been happy wandering in the cranberry bogs, making friends with the berry pickers.

Amos had once liked to reminisce about those summer days of boyhood. He often talked with his friends about the visits. "I took an almighty shine to my grandmother's little house. No matter how rich I am, I'm going to end my days rocking on that piazza." He would chuckle and nod his head in remembrance. But he did not end his days rocking on the cottage piazza, for one day his wife, in a fit of rage, tore the house down, literally, and scattered the gingerbread piazza trim to the four winds.

For two years, Alta traveled in Europe, taking her mother along, whom she treated almost as a maidservant. She made many alleged friendships, especially among those who were useful for her social aspirations. Packing cases from abroad arrived constantly at the Burlington house but were never opened, until eventually the place resembled nothing so much as a warehouse.

One day, out of the blue, the now glittering Mrs. Amos Lawson reappeared in Burlington. The accumulated packing boxes were ripped apart, and soon the high-ceilinged old rooms, so long furnished sparsely and with almost Quaker simplicity by Amos, took on the lurid opulence of a Paris bordello. All her life, Alta's taste was rich and garish; advisers, paid enormous sums to instruct her in what was accepted in society, could not hold her taste in check when she started on a spending spree. In dress, her passion ran to ostrich plumes. Immense bonnets and broad-brimmed hats must be loaded with ostrich plumes, no matter what the immediate fashion was. The cities of Europe were combed for the finest plumes. She wore hats bedecked with ostrich plumes morning, noon, and night. Plume-wearing for Alta, was not only a fetish, it was a personal trademark.

After the fifth or sixth trip to Europe, Alta declared loudly, for anyone to hear, that Burlington and everybody in it bored her to extinction. On one of her trips, she had met a "most charming" architect on board ship. He was—or so he said—an authority on building the castle style of house, the Strawberry Hill Gothic, which was sweeping England. "If one wishes to be in the swim," he told her, "Victorian Gothic is the ticket."

Forthwith, after her sudden attack of Burlington boredom, Alta went to conquer Philadelphia. The Bosworth-Reedy clan loathed her, so she could expect no help from them in establishing herself in the reserved old city, but a Mrs. Culver, whom she had met in Paris, and who, despite her aristocratic family in Philadelphia, seemed always to be in financial straits, would help her arrange an entrance into Philadelphia society—at a price, of course.

Social climbers proverbially flourish, and so flourished Alta Lawson. She built her castle on a commanding knoll in the environs of Philadelphia. And a monstrosity it was, and is, of greenish-gray granite, turreted within an inch of its life. The house was started the day General Robert E. Lee surrendered at Appomattox Courthouse, April 9, 1865. It took three years to build and, save for the grand ball that Alta gave as a housewarming, which turned into a gigantic crush, not only from invited guests but from hordes of curiosity-ridden gate crashers, it was seldom occupied. Sometimes, returning from her frequent trips to Europe, Alta would swoop upon Granite Castle, as the crenelated pile became known locally, give a series of luxurious parties, and then, without a word to anyone, cast off and away to some such spa as Saratoga or White Sulphur Springs, or perhaps go abroad again.

It was just before ground was broken to start building Granite Castle that Alta Lawson played one of the most shameful cards from her devious pack. Yet the play turned out wholly successful, from her warped point of view. She suddenly became extremely friendly, even amorous, toward her woefully neglected husband. Marshaling all her forces, Alta bewitched Amos as she had years before at the church social, wearing a heliotrope silk dress and a flowered green bonnet. If portraits painted of Alta over a period of years by all sorts and conditions of painters present her truly, she was a most bewitching woman. Full-figured, but not too much so, she had a straight, proud carriage, a kind of rakish chic, and a wide, ingratiating smile. In any case, Amos was again completely taken in. Still virile, he made the most of this surprise welcome to the softly lit bedchamber. Then, in a shade over seven months, Alta was delivered of a son.

When a nurse brought the baby into the dining room where Amos was finishing breakfast, he looked at the tiny wrinkled face and laughed heartily. He could scarcely believe his good fortune. A son. A boy to inherit the Lawson Iron Works, just as he had inherited it from his father. Bemused these days, with his wife so mellowed, even considerate of his wishes, he was convinced everything was going to be all right in his household from now on.

Later in the day, he went to see Alta. She smiled at him. "Amos, what do you think of him? I believe he favors you, too. The Lawson forehead. Kiss me, and let me rest again." Amos went softly out of the darkened room, treading on air. Oh yes, surely everything between him and Alta would be wonderful now.

Burlington gossips, like those in any other community, did a good deal of huddling and whispering. Some of the toadies for Alta's favor said, "Well, it does happen sometimes. Why not Alta and Amos Lawson?" A great many Burlingtonians raised their eyebrows and smiled or sneered. Amos, oddly enough, accepted as fact that he was the father of a healthy, loudly bellowing son.

Alta had suffered miserably in labor. Her convalescence was protracted and wearisome. Finally, long drives into the country were prescribed by her doctor. One day, she visited the cottage at Vincentown where Amos had vowed to end his days "rocking on the piazza." The house was old now and the boards of the piazza were rotted by damp. Stepping up to enter the house, she tripped over a loose floor board and fell heavily, giving her ankle a painful twist. In a sudden fury, she called to her coachman to bring her an ax that was standing against a tree in the yard. Blow after blow she rained on the slender columns that supported the piazza roof. Then she grabbed the fragments, the curlicues of wooden fretwork, and threw them onto the lawn. After giving sharp orders to have the house torn down and the debris carted away, she screamed, "I never want to lay eyes on this shabby little cabin again!" Then she limped painfully to her carriage, and was driven back to Burlington.

A few months after this episode, Amos, greatly aged in appearance, started building the house that was to be called Locust Grove, the bleak house wherein he was to suffer mental derangement, prisonlike confinement, and a lonely death, where the Furies were to ride the rafters shrieking a bedlam obbligato to the frenzied screams of a woman tortured beyond all bearing.

Planned by a Philadelphia architect named Pardew, Locust Grove was in the style known as Southern Colonial. This consisted of a high-fronted building of two tall stories and a stone basement with a narrow flight of banistered steps leading to the front door. A steeply raked roof, gabled at both ends, increased the height of the frontage. Five peaked dormers were let into the roof and four massive brick chimneys rose importantly against the green foliage of the locusts. Two one-and-a-half-story wings flanked the central block of the house when it was first erected. These later disappeared. The flat roof of each wing was ringed by a white-painted iron grille in a design of grapevines. Although a measure of style was given the brick chimneys by a series of five-pointed iron stars set into the brickwork, the windows of Locust Grove, which were tall and narrow, did not fit in with the wide proportions of the design.

From the very first, this house must have had an air of brooding, a secretive, withdrawn look. Certainly now, with shudderings of over half a century of human misery whispering behind its walls, the old Lawson place repels one, even in broad daylight.

During the years that Amos Lawson was living a secluded life at Locust Grove, giving over, perforce, the entire management of his foundry and shipyards, men engaged by his wife were doing things *her* way. His alleged son, Lambert Lawson, was growing up in Italy. Alta had rented a villa in Florence, where the boy lived from an early age under the care of a score of servants, nurses, and an English governess. Part of each year, Mrs. Lawson was in residence at the villa, which was named Villa Avellana, for the tall, quivering filbert trees that made green shade on the upper terrace. Later on, people wondered how the boy came to be named Lambert. The name did not appear in the roster of either his father's or his mother's family. Perhaps, some worldly-wise ones ventured, Alta wished to perpetuate the memory of an exceptionally pleasant dalliance. If asked the reason, as she sometimes was, Lambert's mother smiled, shrugged her shoulders, and replied, "I like the name. That is all that matters."

The boy, so carefully tended by a retinue at the Tuscan villa, grew tall and handsome in a leonine sort of way, resembling neither Amos nor Alta Lawson in the slightest degree. He was a moody boy, given to wild fits of temper, and seemed to have no will of his own; his mother or tutors, of which there was a constantly changing file, did his thinking for him. In short, Lambert Lawson was very unstable, a neurotic at the age of eighteen.

In that year, Alta brought her son to the Vincentown house to see his father, for Lambert was heir to all Amos's holdings and it was time he showed himself in his native land. The meeting between father and son accomplished nothing. At this time, Amos was skeletal in appearance, ill and wasted from a paralytic stroke. The young man, standing uneasily before his father, found no recognition; he might have been any young man on earth. Lambert took one look at his father, gasped, and fled the room.

The next day, Alta took Lambert to her social stronghold, Granite Castle, and, in a series of elaborate soirees, introduced him to Philadelphia society. He soon forgot his unhappy father.

For five years, Lambert lived "the rich life" with a vengeance. He traveled a good deal, for goading restlessness bulked large in his nature. He ranged Europe. The fashionable watering places in America knew him, and always he was the Prince Imperial, profligate to the wide.

As in all major things in Lambert Lawson's life, it was his mother who chose a wife for him—chose her and schooled her in just the way she wanted the wife of her rich, fashionable son to conduct herself. The girl she selected was a niece of the aristocratic, perennially moneyless Mrs. Culver, whom Alta Lawson had picked up and befriended in Paris before the Granite Castle phase.

Sophie Dandridge, the girl selected, was the daughter of Mrs. Culver's sister, an ambitious woman who had married a Virginia scion, of a haughty but impoverished family, and, later on, found herself left with four fairly pretty daughters with no dowries. Between the maneuvering of the sisters Dandridge and Culver, a marriage was arranged with Sophie, the eldest daughter, to everyone's satisfaction—except, perhaps, Lambert's, but he had grown listless and far too fond of the bottle by this time to care.

The marriage ceremony and festivities were brilliant. Amos, of course, did not attend, for he was now almost a nonentity, as far as his wife and son were concerned. His days were spent in a semidarkened room at Locust Grove with a male nurse in attendance.

And then, almost overnight, disaster struck. The Lawson Iron Works failed, and on the heels of this catastrophe a bank in Baltimore took over the Lawson shipyards, in Wilmington. It was found that everything under the black, comet-tailed star, trademark of the Lawson enterprises, was mortgaged to the hilt. Years of colossal extravagance on the part of Alta, and later her son, had drained the resources of the lucrative business Amos Lawson had built. But then all management had been out of Amos's hands for many years, and the men whom Alta had placed as her confidential managers had been busy feathering their nests from whatever was left.

First, the Burlington house, with all its garish clutter of lusters, Turkish rugs, and trashy ornaments, was sold for mortgages. Next, Granite Castle went under the hammer. Although this edifice was an architectural monstrosity for the ages, it was the pride of Alta Lawson's heart. The crushing loss of her social stronghold spiked all her dreams for triumphing in society. She promptly withdrew from the world.

Then, almost like the last act of a Greek tragedy, four persons found themselves thrown together under the same roof, in a house in a lonely grove of locust trees. A silent, almost empty house, inhabited, if one could call it that, by the ghost of a once powerful, important, kindly man, a man with no mind left, brought to this pass by two of the members of the frantic three who must henceforth live here or starve: Lambert, son to this man as far as the world knew; Sophie, his young, ineffectual wife; and Alta, a wrathful, hysterical mother, and wife to a senile wreck of a man. She, of the lot, would never be beaten to earth, for her pride and hate would sustain her.

For a while, it is told in Vincentown, an attempt was made to maintain some kind of household at Locust Grove. Mrs. Lawson managed, no one knew how, to keep a carriage and pair. On Sundays, she would drive out alone for an hour or so, richly dressed, her head always surmounted by a bonnet of purple velvet, a veritable forest of purple and cream-colored ostrich plumes waving in the breeze. Rarely was she seen on the street of the village. If she did walk out, she never spoke to anyone she chanced to meet. Marketing was done by a taciturn Irishwoman who had worked for Amos for years and who, for a while, until Amos died, stayed on as sole servant in the house.

Two years after the crash, Amos Lawson was buried in the family plot in Burlington. After that, life seemed to close down completely at Locust Grove. Lights were seldom seen, for the windows were heavily curtained. The carriage and team of horses were sold. An ominous, monumental calm settled around the House of Lawson. On Sundays, Mrs. Lawson, in plumed bonnet and bead-embroidered mantua, relics of her great days, accompanied by her son and daughter-in-law in faded, outmoded finery, would walk slowly down one side of the long, tree-shaded street of Vincentown, turn around at the canal bridge, and return to Locust Grove on the opposite side of the street. The trio talked guardedly among themselves, and seemed oblivious to the people they met.

On weekdays, all three of the Lawsons—Alta, Lambert and Sophie—were to be seen working in a truck garden at one side of the house—a large well-tended garden, which apparently provided most of the food for the family. Lambert, when sober enough to do his share, was dressed in faded garments like a field hand. At first, the two women were neat, in dark, sensible gingham dresses kirtled up under denim aprons. Wide, shady hats of cheap straw, devoid of trimming, all but hid their faces, and there was no sign of hoops or, in later years, bustles, which the pair affected on Sundays, managing to keep as nearly as possible in the mode.

The arching years of hard work and grim poverty seemed to take little toll of Alta's appearance. She aged, of course, but gradually. Not so with Lambert and Sophie. In his face the years were hard felt; in hers was the gauntness of abiding sorrow. He became a habitual drunkard, bleary-eyed, shambling, sometimes shouting obscenities at passersby from the tall, narrow, cobwebbed windows of his foundering house. Often at night, villagers passing the iron gate could hear wild screams and ravings, like those of a man in torment of delirium tremens. Finally, no one saw him in the garden or on the street at all.

Then came the time when it was only Mrs. Lawson and Sophie who walked down one side of the street and back up the other, on the defiant Sunday constitutional, decked out in ostrich plumes and matted velvet dolmans. Gossips in the town relied on news brought by Ezra Colby, the handyman. Lambert had become an alcoholic recluse, spending a large part of the time in bed. What kind of deal he had made with the rapscallion moonshiners who worked stills hidden in the cranberry bogs caused much speculation in the village. How he paid for the oceans of deadly-raw brew that he swilled for thirty years still remains a mystery.

Somewhere around 1890, when Alta Lawson was a gaunt old woman, hindered in her proud stride by rheumatism, she began taking her Sunday walks alone. At first, some said Sophie, worn out by drudgery and by ill-treatment from her bestial husband, had fled back to her relatives in Philadelphia. "Departed in a closed carriage during the night," rumor had it. But she had not. Sophie was worn out by a malingering congestion that was making her cough her lungs away. Except for occasionally working in the garden, she kept out of sight.

On a cold Sunday evening in December—Christmas Eve it was—old Mrs. Lawson set out on her weekly walk. She wore an ancient fur dolman heavily embroidered with jet beads and a maroon bonnet on which the panache of ostrich plumes, subjected for years to the rigors of the chancy elements, had all but worn away. Not much snow on the ground, she noticed, as she clasped her hands more tightly in the little sealskin muff she carried. "But iron cold in the air," she muttered to herself. "Cold enough to strike a mortal chill to younger bones than mine." She hurried on her way. Someone saw her mount the narrow steps to the porch of Locust Grove, enter the front door, and slam it shut with a resounding bang.

A few hours later, close on to midnight, Ezra Colby, bundled in a greatcoat and muffler against the sharp wind, came along the road in front of the Lawson place. Ezra was out late. His brother Clint, who lived half a mile or so up toward Perryville, was very sick. To relieve Clint's hard-worked wife, Ezra had been sitting vigil at his brother's bedside. Now his mind was on getting home as quickly as possible and into his warm feather bed. "My, my, how this snow does swirl about the dooryards," Ezra mumbled into his wool scarf.

As he came abreast of the front door at the Lawsons', a long, agonized shriek rang out from somewhere in the house, followed by another, longer shriek, then cries of "Help! Help!" The front door was flung open by an unseen hand, left to pound to and fro. More screams mounted on the night wind, long shuddering sobs of stark terror. Two women seemed to be grappling in the doorway. One broke loose, and Ezra saw that it was Sophie Lawson, her gray-streaked hair tangled in wild disorder about her face. Behind her, a man leaped out, Lambert Lawson, his face running with blood as if raked by Sophie's fingernails. For a moment, the light from a hanging lamp in the hall pointed the figures high, then the flames nearly guttered in the wind.

Sophie sank to her knees, and Ezra saw the third dark figure, who had stood half concealed behind the banging door. Dressed in scarlet, her black hair awry, Alta suddenly emerged like an avenging Fury. Her voice rang out above the storm. "Here, Lambert! Here! Strike now—now—*now!*" Into his hand she thrust something with a long handle and a blade that caught the light from the lamp. Lambert, eyes blazing, his mouth writhing words that were whirled away on the wind, swung the ax in a mighty heave. Sophie's head, cloven sheer from her body, leaped into space like a live thing, struck a pillar of the porch, and rolled down the steps, to come to rest at the feet of Ezra Colby.

In the last years of Amos Lawson's life, when he needed the care of a keeper constantly, it is said that he had a passion for playing with squills of paper set alight from candles and lamps. He would carry candles about in the series of dormered attic rooms that were his world, talking animatedly to the shadows cast on the walls. Watched by his nurse, he probably amused himself for hours in a candlelit world of shadowgraph. It is Amos prowling his attic domain with a lighted candle that villagers say they often see at night as fitful, jerky radiances pass the windows. Tramps who sometimes crawl into the deserted house for shelter rarely stop the night; creakings of attic floor boards and ghostly lights moving against mildewed walls drive them out into the open in great alarm.

A pair of students from Rutgers College once tried to spend a weekend in the old house. They were horrified twofold. Grating noises, fitful lights, and sagging doors that banged back and forth against the walls were one thing, more or less what they had been led to expect—in fact, just what was needed for a proposed thesis on the supernatural. But to have the blood curdled in their veins by the most agonizing shrieks of a soul in mortal terror and to see a man sever a woman's head clean off her body in the entrance porch was too much. The youths fled, leaving the notes for the epic thesis behind.

And so it is. For many years, gaunt, disheveled Locust Grove has stood abandoned, unwanted by whoever owns the property. Lambert died in an insane asylum shortly after the Euripidean murder of his wife. Alta Lawson, questioned by town authorities, told a straightforward story that seemed to satisfy them. She had tried to protect her daughter-in-law, who, she said, was in the last stages of consumption. Ezra Colby, had he come forward and told what he saw in the fitful lamplight, could have confounded her story. He did not. On his deathbed he related what he had seen, to ease his conscience. But Alta had been dead for some years by that time. She was beyond the law's reach and could not be punished for inciting the murder—indeed, doing everything but actually swinging the lethal ax.

Alta is said to have gone on working in her garden, raising food to feed herself. On Sundays, she continued to take her constitutionals, but only if the weather was fine. Then she died all alone in the house she had always hated.

It is told that when undertakers arrived to lay out the remains of Alta, they found great disorder. All manner of trashy odds and ends from mail-order houses mixed with mother-of-pearl and papier-mâché boxes, trays, and gilt furniture littered the rooms. One enormous Saratoga trunk, long enough to pack a ball gown *en-train* flat, was filled with unworn gowns, many bearing labels of a famous couturier of Paris. A huge portrait of Alta Lawson, painted in Vienna by Pacher at the zenith of her career as an American millionairess on the *grand tour,* hung, badly torn and varnish-cracked in the library. In the portrait, Alta is standing at the gates of the Prater. A landau with four snowy Lippizaners in the traces waits behind her. The dashing Mrs. Amos Lawson wears a spreading hoop of parma-violet silk, and an immense bonnet encircled by sapphire-blue ostrich plumes. A sword-thrust reminder of great days for Alta to live with, one would think.

One evening at twilight a few years ago, a visitor to Vincentown was walking along the street that leads to Locust Grove when she noticed approaching her a tall figure with an imperious walk, elaborately dressed in a costume of purple with a bustle. Rather startled, she couldn't help staring at the huge bonnet because of a forest of waving, but definitely bedraggled, ostrich plumes that the strangely attired person wore as proudly as an empress wears her crown. The visitor stepped aside to make room on the sidewalk and smiled and nodded her head in greeting to the woman in purple. Giving the friendly visitor no notice, the shade of Alta Cossart Lawson, who had for so many years ridden through life roughshod and contemptuous of others, walked silently on. A memorable ghost surely. On she walked, heavy eyes hooded, chin raised, bosom thrusting arrogantly, an elegant jut to the bustle. Was she reliving her social triumphs at Granite Castle as she disappeared in the failing light, pursuing her eternal constitutional?

Scent of Lilacs
on the Breeze

BUCYRUS, OHIO, 1900

O NCE, in the chilly, seldom-used parlor of a wide-spreading white farmhouse in upper New York State, I saw a picture that has ever since remained in my memory. As I write this story, I can still see the quiet color, feel the tender illusive mood of the painting, its fragility, as though I had just looked at the picture again. But I saw it only once, long ago.

In art circles, the picture would have been termed American primitive. More delicately drawn than most primitives, it contained none of the hardness, the still formality of arrangement, one finds in some portraits—big-eyed children clutching dog or doll, flat-faced women, who might be any age from twenty to sixty, in severe dress with huge breast pin. The treatment was light, gossamer, the subject a rounded young girl, undeniably youthful, in a ruffled white dress and big white hair-ribbon bows. She stood in a grove of slender, palely painted saplings, and I remember there was a bough of white blossoms—fruit blossoms, as I recall—that set the mood for May. It was indeed, a pastoral, a pastiche, a fragment of the utter innocence found in fleeting youth before the world and its ways have intruded. When I asked who the girl was, and who had painted the picture, no one knew. "Father bought the picture at the county fair, because he liked it," one of the women of the house said.

Years later, when I sat in a farmhouse in Ohio, in front of the graying embers of a log fire after an evening of telling tall tales, my mind went back to the painting of the young country girl in white, poised lightly in a sapling wood. A long time had passed since I had seen the picture but how immediate it was in my consciousness! While listening to one of the tales, a ghost story about a girl named Ethel Hanley that had captured and held my imagination by its singularly haunting power, I had thought, Ethel might be the girl in the white ruffled dress pulling down a bough of May blossoms.

On an afternoon in late May, Frank Burbank, a young surveyor, breasted a hill a few miles outside Bucyrus. From the hilltop, he was to look over some fields, owned by a farmer named Hanley, that were being bought by the State Highway Commission.

The day was growing unseasonably hot; spring had come early that year, prodigal with flowers both wild and garden. Daffodils, tulips, and crocuses, long since past blooming, had been replaced by climbing roses, clematis, and syringa, big in bud. Lilacs blew in many dooryards. Lilacs! Now, there was a flower! Frank liked the Persian purples, but, for him, nothing in the flower kingdom could equal the white ones, so plumelike and fragrant.

When Frank reached the top of the hill, he heard voices and laughter from the direction of a white clapboard house that stood a few yards from the road, on his right. Locust trees marched sentinel in front of the house, and a lawn with bushes and a few flower beds lent a pleasant approach. What caught and held his eye, however, was the prettiest girl he had ever seen, standing embowered in a fountain of white lilacs. Now, this is not true, thought Frank. White lilacs and a girl with corn-silk hair, in a ruffly white dress, her arms full of lilacs. Things just didn't happen this way. Then he saw a man standing a few feet in front of the girl, bent over, with a square of black cloth over his head. The man raised his hand in the well-known "watch the birdie" gesture. The girl was having her picture taken.

Unnoticed, Frank viewed the scene. Besides the girl and the photographer, a woman stood in the doorway watching the proceedings, and a small boy and girl stared, goggle-eyed, at the feet of the photographer. Then, with considerable satisfaction, the young surveyor saw a wooden sign nailed to one of the trees, reading, "Cold Buttermilk Served."

No surveying job within Frank's memory had been so thoroughly pleasant as this one. As he handed his long-range glasses to his helper, Ted Davis, and rolled down his sleeves, Frank nodded to the question in Ted's eyes.

"You're right. I'm not going down to Bucyrus with you. I'm going to get my daily glass of buttermilk."

Ted smiled. "I didn't know you liked buttermilk so much."

"It's an acquired taste," Frank said, laughing. "See you later."

"Yes, much later. There's a big moon tonight," Ted said as he took the path down the hill.

At the Hanleys', Frank drank buttermilk and talked to Ethel's brother Sammy and Addie, an orphan cousin who lived with the family. After he had downed his second glass, he stood up hesitantly as if to go. Mrs. Hanley, noticing his reluctance, said, "Sit awhile, Frank. Ethel's sure to be along soon. Her father's driving her home. She's run ragged these days, with the graduation exercises coming up and her dress not finished yet. What you saw the other day was only tacked together for the photograph. She didn't even have her sash. That's coming by mail from a big store in Cincinnati, where her cousin Louella Biggs clerks. She's picking it out."

A little later, Ethel and her father arrived, and, of course, Frank was asked to stay to supper.

After the meal was over, when Frank and Ethel offered to help Mrs. Hanley with the dishes, she waved them away. "Go on, take your walk. Frank, don't keep Ethel out long. Remember she's still a schoolgirl."

The two wandered down through the clover meadow and sat on a stone foundation where a hay barn had once stood. Wild budding roses now covered most of the wall.

Ethel, breaking a silence of some minutes, said, "When do you expect to finish your job of surveying, Frank? I mean when will you be leaving Bucyrus?"

Frank reached over and took Ethel's hand. For a moment, he let the hand lie, whitened by moonlight, on his palm, then he covered it with his other hand, caressingly. "I aim to stay in Bucyrus, Ethel, as long as you want me to." The girl smiled up at him, and he took her in his arms.

Frank went to the graduation exercises and sat with the Hanleys. Ethel who had earned the place of valedictorian, gave the class oration, in her plea ant, soft voice, and Frank, entranced, watched her every move. In her wh organdie dress, with a wide sash of sky-blue ribbon tied in a bow at the si she was the loveliest thing he had ever imagined.

Earlier that day, as they had been leaving the farm, Frank had cut a s

of white lilacs, almost the last, from a big bush beside the front door. Ethel had smiled and tucked it in her sash.

Now, sitting in the audience, he could smell the odor of the lilacs plain as could be. Lilacs and Ethel. One would always remind him of the other.

The next day, Frank asked Mr. Hanley for consent to marry Ethel. Farmer Hanley shook his head. "My boy, she's too young to marry you or anybody else. Ethel's only seventeen. I like you. I'd like you for a son-in-law. You're steady, you're temperate, and you're good-natured. But you and my daughter'll have to wait. Wait two years. Ethel's mother was nineteen when I married her. It's a good age to start life off together. Are you going to stay in the surveyor's office in Bucyrus?"

Frank was silent with disappointment for a moment. "No," he said, finally. "I'm studying to be a civil engineer. If I wait two years, Mr. Hanley, will you give your consent?"

Mr. Hanley nodded. "Yes, my son, I certainly will."

Frank Burbank was twenty-eight when he went to Cincinnati to study engineering. To earn money for his keep, he took a job working on the night shift of a daily newspaper. He was even able to put by a little. In his small boarding-house room, on a table close to his bed, stood the framed photograph of a smiling girl with soft blond hair, in white, with lilacs in her arms. It was the graduation picture. Every night, Frank gazed at Ethel's face and smelled again the scent of lilacs.

Meanwhile, Ethel settled into taking charge of the many chores at the farm. Twice a week, she wrote to Frank. Oftener than that, he wrote to her. Then, two years later to the day, he packed his bag and went back to Bucyrus, a full-fledged engineer.

Ethel met him at the train with the buggy, and after a happy reunion they started on their way. As they drove up the hill near the Hanley farm, the horse shied a number of times, seemingly at nothing.

"You've got a new horse, I see," Frank said. "What's he shying at all the time?"

Ethel laughed. "He's a silly. Aren't you, Bill? He shies at his own shadow."

Frank arrived on a Thursday. After a talk with Mr. Hanley, it was arranged that Frank and Ethel would be married in two weeks, on her birthday, the fifth of June.

The following Sunday, Mr. Hanley drove his wife to church in Greggsville, a small village three miles from the farm in the opposite direction from Bucyrus. Ethel, Frank, and Sammy stayed home to prepare dinner. Addie was visiting a friend on a neighboring farm.

In the afternoon, Ethel asked her father if Bill was too used up for a drive. She wanted to take Frank to see a small house on the Mansfield road. It was for sale—a nice little place. She had seen it first some months ago.

"No, Bill's not too tired," her father answered. "That horse beats me. He's twelve years old, but he's as skittish at times as a two-year-old. Better let Frank drive."

The day was warm and still; hardly a breath of air was stirring. Ethel went up to her room under the eaves. She had a surprise for Frank—a new white dress with lots of lace-edged ruffles on the waist, just the kind of dress he liked her in. She had a new hat, too,—pale-blue straw—and for fun she pinned a spray of white lilacs among the blue ribbon loops.

When she came downstairs in her finery, she was a great success; Frank's eyes shone as he admired her. Proudly, he helped her into the buggy, and they set off along the turnpike, with Frank at the reins. Apple-blossoms were turning brown and so were lilacs in many dooryards. It had been another long, warm spring and flowers were early over. Bill seemed on his good behavior, jogging along so quietly that Frank could relax and look at the scenery. They passed the old Spear place, run to ruin now since the Spear boys had chosen to live in Mansfield. The Murdock place looked neat as a new pin.

"Nice place the Murdocks have," Frank said. "One day, we'll have one even better." Then he had to pull Bill over to let a rig pass. A girl with fiery-red hair and a big green bow on her hat waved to them from the front seat of a fringed-top surrey.

"Hello, Ethel!" she called.

"Hello, Zella! Come over and see me." Ethel turned to Frank. "That's Zella Murdock, a school friend of mine. You met her, remember? At the graduation dance."

"I saw only one girl at the dance. We should make a wish. The first red-haired girl driving a white horse we've seen today. Good luck, you know." Frank laughed and turned his attention to a tall mass of bright-red paint on the other side of the road from the Murdock place.

"Farmer Hawkes has built a new silo," Ethel told him.

Now they were coming to a downgrade. At the bottom of the hill, a stone bridge spanned a reed-choked stream, little more than a brook. Just as Frank started to tighten the reins, a boy riding a bicycle shot out from a side road to the right of the highway. Bill shied violently, snorted, reared, and leaped forward, snapping the whippletree. Plunging down the grade, the maddened animal swung the light buggy against a stone parapet, smashing a wheel. Ethel was thrown clear, struck her head on the coping of the bridge, and died immediately.

After Ethel's funeral, Frank Burbank left Bucyrus. For three years, he wandered about from city to city. Once, he accepted an engineering job in Alaska. Perhaps, thought Frank, if I get far enough away, I can shake the thoughts of that terrible Sunday afternoon from my mind. But six months in Nome did not help. It seemed to the harassed young man that never, waking or sleeping, was his mind free of the thought of Ethel, lying crumpled in his arms, stained with blood.

One day, Frank sat down at the desk in the Antlers Hotel, in Winnipeg, and wrote to his old boss, Will Taylor, in Bucyrus. Was there an opening in the State Highway Commission office? Anything would do; he did not care.

For a while after Frank returned to Bucyrus, he lived quietly, surveying a bit, keeping the office accounts, and, on Sundays, taking long walks alone in the foothills.

One day in October, when the masses of slashing color in sumac, sassafras, and maple were dazzling with brilliance, Frank was hailed as he crossed the highway.

A young woman driving a buggy called out, "Hello. Aren't you Frank Burbank?"

He nodded. "Thought I recognized you," she said. "I'm Zella Murdock. If you're going into Bucyrus, let me give you a lift."

"Well, thank you, Miss Murdock, but I'm going to supper at the Hanleys'."

"Get in, I'll drive you there."

Later that night, after Frank had walked down the hill toward Bucyrus, Mrs. Hanley said, "Pa, I'm worried about Frank. Since he came back, he's changed so. Almost never smiles. Doesn't seem to hear what a body says to him. Seems always listening or watching for someone. And he did such a funny thing. When I was bidding him good night at the door, he walked over to that lilac bush by the millstone. It's bare as your hand now. He broke off a twig and passed it back and forth under his nose. Then he looked at me as if he didn't see me at all. I could hardly hear him as he turned away. He sort of whispered, 'The smell of lilacs is strong tonight.'"

The marriage of Zella Murdock, who, everybody allowed, "would come into plenty when old Jeff Murdock died," to Frank Burbank surprised few of the townspeople of Bucyrus or the farmers who lived in the valley and along the Mansfield road. Zella was a tartar, the local swains admitted. She got what she wanted. She wanted Frank Burbank. But Zella herself was probably never aware that all she got was the big-framed body of Frank to father her children. Never did she capture his heart or share his thoughts.

Zella was a busy woman. Her big house ran like oiled machinery. She had plenty of help to look after the three children that came along in as many years. After this spate of maternity, Zella decided to call a halt. Two boys and a girl were enough. Thereafter she devoted her life to her various clubs and social activities. Once she had roped Frank and he had performed his duties as consort, Zella left him to his own devices, feeling reasonably sure he would not cause her any anxiety.

In the years before the death of Ethel Hanley, the role of husband to a rich wife, even one as attractive as Zella, would never have interested Frank Burbank. At the time he had had ambitions to attain a high place in the world of civil engineering. But the Frank who wandered aimlessly across the hills and valley of the Scioto River had changed greatly since the night in May when he had sat upon a rose-hung stone foundation telling a schoolgirl that he loved her. The new Frank was a distracted man who followed a phantom in every sense of the word.

One of the first things Frank did on his own after he went to live at Murdock Farm was to buy white-lilac bushes. Some he bought from nurserymen who cultivated them; some he bought straight out of farmers' dooryards; and some he took from derelict old places back in the hills, where lone orchards, run to rank grass and dead apple trees, and moss-grown hollows of stone told of dwellings long burned away.

"What on earth you want with so many lilacs, I fail to see," Zella scoffed. "They keep him amused, anyhow," she said, shrugging to a visitor taking tea.

One day, Frank went up to the Hanley place to help unload fertilizer. It was March and a chill wind blew about the hilltop. When the work was finished, dusk had laid soft shadows all about, heralding night. As Frank was about to get into his buggy, he thought he saw a woman standing down by the old hay-barn foundations. He tied his reins around a hitching post and started down the path. The first intimation of what he would find was—almost undiscernible—the scent of lilacs. Unconsciously, he looked back over his shoulder. The big lilac bush was scarcely in bud. Bare and brown spread the branches.

Standing in what had once been the door to a byre in the old stone barn was a young girl in a white dress and a wide blue hat. She smiled gently at Frank, who paused, stockstill, halfway up the path. Then he uttered a cry of terrible loneliness and ran toward the apparition, but in the darkening night the figure faded away. For a long while, Frank remained leaning against the stone wall.

November set in dry and cool. Shooting was exceedingly fine that year. Quail and partridge were plentiful. Frank took his gun and a setter out for a few hours. Walking through a dense thicket half-circling the foot of the hill on which the Hanley farm lay, the hunter whistled to his dog. "Come on, Sport, flush 'em—" He stopped in mid-command.

Coming down the hill, slowly, almost floating, as if her feet need not touch the ground, was a figure of a girl in white. Although myriad branches and twigs crosshatched the path along which she moved, not one bent in the slightest degree to allow her to pass. The apparition in white passed through the sharp branches as though they were a wall of mist.

Sport crouched, every hackle standing, at his master's feet, and emitted short, low whines and beat the dry leaves on the path with his forepaw. For a space of minutes, the tableau held—the hunter, trembling dog, and the woman in luminous white. She stood on the russet path, pierced, as it were, by a hundred sapling twigs. And eddying across the field, a light wind carried the scent of May.

Frank never knew, through the years, where or at what time of day or night he would suddenly encounter the delicate ghost of Ethel Hanley and her aura. He asked Mrs. Hanley in a roundabout way if she had ever been conscious of the presence of her daughter.

"Once, I thought I saw a girl in white walking down by the old hay-barn wall," she said. "But I guess it was a trick of the moonlight." She smiled wistfully.

On the night of the eighteenth birthday of Frank's daughter Joan, a dinner dance was held in celebration. Just before the festivities, Frank came downstairs and found his daughter, in apple-green silk, standing by the bay window in the dining room.

"You look very pretty tonight, Joan," Frank said, and put his arm across her shoulders.

After a slight pause, she said, "I want to tell you something, Daddy. I have been sure, for the last hour, that a woman is walking around out there in the garden. There, by that hedge of white lilac—the big ragged bushes you transplanted from those old places in the hills. I thought at first it was one of the girls from town playing a trick on me. But when I went out to look, not a soul was in sight. It must be Mother's Scottish ancestors rising in me. You know 'seventh daughter of seventh daughter,' born with a caul, and all that. But I could have sworn I saw a young girl in a white dress and a big hat sort of floating in and out of those lilacs."

The doorbell rang, and she turned away, her attention diverted, to greet her guests. Frank took her place at the window and stood at the window, watching, until Zella came bustling in to fetch him.

After dinner, more guests came, and dancing began. Frank saw that Zella, an untiring hostess, was in high fettle, so he slipped out into the soft, mild night. How many May moons he had seen just like this and how unbearably lonely it always made him.

For a time, he walked about aimlessly. Then he struck off along the little brook that ran past the foot of the hill. About a mile away, he could see a light in the Hanley kitchen. Walking on, unthinking, Frank realized he had come to the thick wood of underbrush and saplings where the hill started to rise. Suddenly, he caught his breath. For, there, moving with that delicately floating motion he had come to know so well, was the figure in white. Tonight the manner was different. Arms held out at the sides, the white phantom seemed to be moving through the measures of a dance.

Frank started forward. Tonight Ethel must not elude him. He could not bear this longing. As he sprang up the hill, the figure floated backward, backward. Now he fought the thick tangle of branches in a frenzy. Always the floating girl in white receded farther up the hillside. Then she lifted her hand and seemed to toss something onto the leaf mold at his feet. He stooped to pick it up, and when he straightened, the figure was gone. Scarcely believing, Frank looked at what he had retrieved from the ground—a spray of white lilacs, as fresh as if it had just been cut.

THE REPROBATES

AMERICANA OF THE DIVES AND HIGHWAYS

Bella Rawhide and Timber Kate

SPOKANE AND CARSON CITY, 1880

IN ALL the annals of debauchery in roistering gold-coast gambling dens and roaring mining-town saloons, none glares more outrageously, albeit sometimes humorously, than the saga of two "sisters," Bella Rawhide and Timber Kate.

This glittering pair were known from Spokane to Santa Fe. Except for a ten-year interval, when Bella, after a mighty battle with Timber, went to Carson City and ran a whorehouse of her own, they were almost inseparable. For some years during the split-up, Timber Kate, a gigantically tall woman of great strength, worked her con game alone. An unusual feature of her approach was her use of haymakers, which she employed in place of the knockout drops usually administered to male clients by harlots. The punch in the jaw that Timber Kate delivered at the drop of the hat was never equalled, or so the receivers said, by any pugilist before or since.

Whether these girls were actually blood sisters or not doesn't signify. Sister acts on the stages of saloons and in bawdyhouse demonstrations were the style; it was in the cards that these two should claim to be sisters. In Bella's last days when she was never sober and all her mottled past rose up to confront her, she would,

33

when on the verge of delirium tremens, shout to all and sundry that Timber Kate was not her sister at all, but her mother.

"The big old sow!" Bella would cry. "She set me to work in the mining camps when I was a brat! I supported her for years! Rot her! Lemme at her! Where is she?" Then a wild chase would ensue, ending usually in bloody heads and broken bottles.

The first time Bella Rawhide and Timber Kate danced in a saloon in Spokane, not only the floor boards sagged but the rafters rang with the tumult of sound from their combined voices. Timber roared like a bull and Bella screeched like a chimpanzee. Such caterwauling had never been heard before, even in the roughest dives, and the robust characters who frequented these dens loved it. Overnight, this pair of females in red tights and gold spangles made a tremendous hit. The songs they sang were for men only. After their nightly performance on the boards, the vitality of their behavior on the mattresses was unique. No doubt about it, Bella and Timber were the rage.

Bella, a medium-sized natural honey blonde, had big, bulging blue eyes and a loose-lipped mouth. Timber Kate, who stood six feet six in bare feet, was muscular as a stevedore and as raucous of voice. She sported an unruly shock of carrot-red curls, and her eyes, which were muddy brown, had a hard gleam in their depths. The one feature the two had in common was the mouth. Loose and big in Bella's face, in Timber's it opened like an immense gulch.

The way the sisters differed most was in temper. Bella, during most of her life, was as agreeable as a sunny May morning, with a wide smile of welcome for all men and most women. Timber Kate was a horse of another color. She hated everybody, or so she liked to yell— "Bring 'em on, the bastards! Stand 'em up, and Timber'll knock 'em down so fast it'll make your hair curl!"

A fight was what Timber was on the lookout for, twenty-four hours a day. Nevertheless, she proved to be a good business-woman, in contrast to Bella, who was the prize pushover. "I always get their money first, before I hang them on their shadow with my special punch. I never lose," Timber said.

Up and down the trails, following the prospectors' towns, Bella and Timber rolled. Towns that were built in a day blared forth in improbable prosperity for a while and became ghost towns as quickly as they had risen.

Bella and Timber were always in demand, because they had an original viewpoint in entertainment. Just before their ten-year separation, Bella staged a dance that sent the audience wild. She came on the stage clothed in green spangle fig leaves and nothing else. For a small pouch of gold-dust, a man could remove a spangle leaf. The fellow who removed the last leaf could carry her off to bed. The finale of this dance, called "Eve's Leaves," was the high note in border entertainment.

For the most part, Timber did not care for men. She made no bones about it. Prostitution was her trade. "Same as a dishwasher," she would say. "Nobody rightly likes to wash greasy dishes. But it's a livin'. Same way I feel about whorin'."

Then came Tug Daniels on the scene. The guffaws that were raised on his appearance at the Red Shiner saloon, in Phoenix, rang loud and clear until, in a surprise move, he drilled a prospector in the shoulder, "Jest fer quiet, ye understand," said Tug, a little, weaselly, bowlegged critter from nowhere. Nobody knew him or had ever heard anything about him. He dressed in the garish style often affected by the half-breed Mexican pimps who trafficked in Carson City and Butte and as far west as Spokane. A rat face, lank black hair worn in greasy, pointed sideburns, a mouthful of ragged yellow teeth, and a leathery yellow skin riddled with pockmarks added little to his charm. One feature, however, arrested the beholder— huge liquid brown eyes, the eyes of a lovesick Mexican señorita. Tug was not one to neglect the value of the romantic eyes he had inherited from his Mexican mother. He used them as the cobra uses its forked tongue.

Tug was a killer. But he took what he wanted first. He had heard by the desert grapevine that Bella and Timber were rich from a long, highly successful career. He proposed to take them one at a time. What he did not bank on was that both women would fall for him, one with a young girl's romantic enthusiasm, the other with venomous passion.

That Bella should succumb to Tug's weedy masculine charms was not too surprising. But it was Timber, three-quarters masculine and wary as a badger, who went after him whole hog. From the first, her livid jealousy was apparent. When Tug Daniels decided to seduce Bella first, and paid her open court, Timber raged in anger. A few nights after Tug's arrival at the Red Shiner, he danced with Bella, who had dressed the part of enchantress to the hilt. In bright-purple satin, looped with orange silk poppies, she filled the eye to overflowing. Tug grasped her by both hips and sailed out onto the dance floor. Timber, who was sitting at a side table tossing off straight whiskeys with the regularity of the drummer's beat, finally blew her top. Leaping up, she pushed Tug aside and grabbed Bella by the throat.

Such a public trouncing as she gave Bella had not been seen in many moons, certainly not administered by one woman to another. With a final fling, Timber Kate tossed Bella, now unconscious, against the wall and ran up the stairs to her room, roaring, "Don't no damned skunk of a man follow me! D'ya hear? I'm closed for the night!"

The aftermath of this affair was Bella's departure, for Carson City, accompanied by Tug Daniels. With her savings, she bought and ran a fancy bawdyhouse, the Bee Hive, in the red-light district of the railroad junction. For a while, Tug lived off Bella, but eventually, as she had suspected would happen, he ran off with her money box.

From the time of the quarrel between the sisters, Timber began to disintegrate. She took up with two or three women of her kidney in various mining towns. But the originality of the sister act was no more. For a while, Timber, dressed as a man, in white tights and a leopard-skin shirt, did a weight-lifting act. But that did not take on, because she raged against the razzing from bored onlookers. "Hey, big girl, strip!" the men would yell. "Come on, sister, let's see what ye've got where ye ain't got what we got!" The strong-man act was a flop.

Then, one night, a huge woman, dressed in a sombrero and dogie-skin chaps, arrived at the Bee Hive whorehouse, on Quincy Street, Carson City. It was Timber Kate. She and Bella reconciled, and Timber asked to join the ranks of prostitutes in the fancy-priced Bee Hive. The next morning, a colored maid found the two, stone drunk, on the floor of Bella's room.

But Timber's jealous rages flared high more and more often. Things were going from bad to worse at the Bee Hive when Tug again appeared on the scene. He couldn't have timed it better for a showdown. It was a Saturday night in spring; the house, jammed at ten o'clock, would be even fuller until dawn. Girls in thin wrappers, with colored taffeta bows in their pompadours, were running to and fro from the big mirrored parlor, as busy as the bees the house was named for. "God, I'm dead on me feet already," chirped one blond. "You'll be dead on yer back before mornin'," answered a bold mulatto.

Tug had not worn well with his traipsing. Neither had Bella, who was fat, raddled, and sloppy. And certainly Timber Kate was a scarecrow of her former, magnificently upholstered self. The three gazed at each other. Timber made a lunge to hang one of her well-known haymakers on the little ratlike man. But Tug was too quick for her, his agility in pulling a knife was lightning swift. Before Timber knew what had hit her, he had ripped her belly wide open from crotch to navel. Screaming like a jackal, she fell like all the timber in the primeval forests of the world. She lay, dying, in a pool of blood as Tug smashed through a back window and made his escape.

Two years after this tragedy, Bella Rawhide shut herself in her room one night. In the morning, she was dead from a dose of cleaning fluid.

In the days when Bella Rawhide and her sister Timber Kate were working their act, it was always Timber who went around the towns where they played, putting up posters. The favorite with the public seemed to be one depicting an enormous Timber, in red tights and gold spangles, holding Bella, dressed as a pink rose, in the palm of her outstretched hand.

After the deaths of the two women, these posters began to turn up on walls of buildings in Carson City, Cheyenne, Butte, and Spokane—all cities that had given the sisters welcome. One night, the owner of a tobacco store situated on a corner in Carson City shut up shop rather later than usual. As he turned the corner, he became conscious of a figure of immense height standing beside the side wall, a large, windowless brick surface. He moved forward cautiously and saw that it was a woman, in a short skirt, high Western boots, and a sombrero, busily engaged in pasting a poster on the wall. When the man approached, the woman faded into the night. Amazed, he stood looking at the poster; it was a vivid advertisement of a musical act by Bella Rawhide and Timber Kate. The man started to peel the poster from the wall but was stopped decisively by a tremendous blow on the back of his neck. Hours afterward, he was found, still unconscious, lying where he had been struck down.

Another report of the apparition of Timber Kate comes from Washington State. In a former mining town near Spokane, there is a building that was at one time the local opera house. Old newspapers show that the building had previously been a famous honky-tonk. One night, a caretaker saw two women—one very tall, the other of medium size—dancing on the bare stage. The tall one was dressed in scarlet tights and spangles. The other, in gaudy pink ruffles, would leap up onto the palm of the hand of the woman in red. The caretaker switched on the lights, and the pair immediately disappeared.

Many times in the slums of Carson City, people tell of having seen a fat, bloated woman in a ragged white nightgown stumbling along the street. The creature seems in agony, clawing at her mouth and throat. She staggers along and slips into a dark doorway, out of sight.

Timber Kate, always the stronger of the sisters, pursues the activities she pursued in life. Poor Bella concentrates on her last agonized moments which she spent alone, behind locked doors, in her busy Bee Hive.

Tall Spendthrift, Short Miser
Thin Murderer, Fat Thief

VERMONT, 1830

HAD BELLA RAWHIDE and her sister Timber Kate lived at the time of the four characters whose story I am about to relate, the six would have made a fabulous group in flashing underworld history. Brilliant and bawdy as were the sisters, these four rapscallions—Terrance Blunt, Andrew Marr, Cal Longstreet, and Frank Ballard—did much to secure the honors for vice and skulduggery in the field of masculine effort. Perhaps they have become acquainted by now in some plushy glade in space, call it Hell, Time, Middle Mist, or even Purgatory, where the damned are supposed to writhe. All six met sudden deaths. All were pitched agonizingly into eternity. The lot of them had much in common.

Somewhere about 1820, a tall, exquisitely dressed young man named Terrance Blunt stole ten thousand dollars from his father, in Baton Rouge. In the dead of night, he lit out from under the white pillared portico of his birthplace, a mansion called Melbourne, and his father never saw him again.

Around this time, a short, thickset cardsharp, one Andrew Marr, of Scottish descent, buried a fortune in ill-gotten gains—mostly from cheating at cards or swindling gullible note signers—in a woods near Rochester, New York. Then he, too, set out on an unchartered journey.

Perhaps it was on the same night, or close to it, that a beautiful woman was murdered in San Francisco. The murderer, a cadaverously thin man with the face of a Botticelli angel, was Calvin Longstreet. Some years before, his mother had

39

been the most-talked-of actress in London. But Cal was obsessed by the desire to kill. One night, after the opening of her most successful play, LaSalle Longstreet, as she was known to London audiences, retired, somewhat fatigued, to bed. During the night, her twenty-year-old son strangled her with a silk scarf. Why? No reason. He just had to kill beautiful females. After robbing his mother's purse of enough money for flight to a new country, he had left the house. The San Francisco murder was one of a series, for which he had never been caught.

Not long afterward, an innkeeper by the name of Monroe, in Des Moines, was putting his day's receipts away when he was set upon and beaten by a masked intruder—Frank Ballard—who had slipped in by a cellar window. For all his fatness, no thief could gain entrance to inns, farmhouses, or city mansions with the cleverness of Fat Frank, as his cronies called him. Fat Frank was a mongrel. Ballard was not his name; he never had known a surname. Once, in Kentucky when he had robbed the office of a feed store, he had hastily crammed his loot into a sack. The next morning, gliding down the Ohio River in a cat canoe, he had noticed the name in red letters, stenciled on the bag, and decided that since it sounded highfalutin, he'd take it. He was Frank Ballard from then on.

Slowly, each in his own way leaving a trail of disaster in his wake, these four reprobates were converging on one spot in the green-mountained state of Vermont.

The Fates did not hurry them. Over a period of fifteen years, the four men were played on invisible lines, like trout in a sun-dappled stream; the lines, strong as spider gossamer, formed a web of immense scope. From state to state, city to city, the men wove their pernicious ways. News did not travel fast in the days before transcontinental railways and the telegraph. But travelers by stagecoach, or riders carrying bulletins and letters in saddlebags, spread news of robberies, satanic murders, swindles on a grand scale, and the antics of a handsome fellow who gambled for high stakes and then, in one fell swoop, spent the proceeds entertaining some enchantress.

Terrance Blunt raised his aching head from a silk pillow in the bridal suite of Sanderson's Hotel, in Toledo. He had gambled extravagantly the night before. In two days, his winnings would be spent. What matter. Terrance rolled his long, lithe body across the bed and took the golden-haired girl lying next to him in his arms, kissing her awake. "Oh, hello," she said. "Say, what's your name? You never told me."

With a rather shaky finger, he jiggled the diamonds of a necklace, which, at the moment, was all she wore. "Good stones." Terrance kissed her eyelids. "Cost a hell of a lot of cash, those sparklers. Le's see if you're worth it."

In an office on a dingy street in Cleveland, Andrew Marr pocketed a fat roll of currency, stuffing it into his greatcoat pocket. He looked coldly at the shivering man who stood, spread-eagled, against a wall of the room. Andrew said, in a low voice, "I told you I'd be back for my cut, you foolish ape. If I wasn't so good-natured, you know you might get hurt."

The other man seemed to regain control of himself for a minute. "I won't set no more stores afire, Saturday nor any other day!" he shouted. "What do I get out of it? *You* get it all in the end. Besides, three fires in a month is too much. The sheriff's—"

Andrew hit the man across the mouth. "You'll do as I say! You'll set that fire Saturday!" He patted the roll of bills in his pocket, slammed the door, and walked importantly down the street.

"Rotten miser, miser, miser!" shouted the man.

A beautiful woman named Frances Norfield, riding in a victoria along the river road near Holyoke, wondered if the young man she had met at a party the night before would call on her as he had promised. Longstreet, wasn't that his name? So tall and thin, but such a beautiful head. Like pictures of Shelley and Byron. And his voice and manner were so arresting. A bit theatrical, perhaps, but a delightful change. As the coachman turned the team in to the driveway of Rosemont, her home, she sighed. "Perhaps I've made a conquest. Oh, I do hope he comes."

After a solitary supper off a tray in her boudoir, Mrs. Norfield, gleaming exquisitely in a rosy chiffon peignoir, with fresh lilacs in her ash-blond hair, settled down to read. Shortly, a maid entered and announced, "Mr. Longstreet, Madam," and her smiling admirer arrived.

About two o'clock in the morning, he left via a French window and was soon swallowed up in the foliage of the spruce grove bordering Frances Norfield's garden. Or, rather, the late Frances Norfield. For the next morning, when the maid brought in her mistress's morning chocolate, she stumbled over the body of the once lovely Frances, purple of face, tongue protruding from gaping lips, strangled with a thin silk scarf.

"Damn it, I'm gettin' old, and fatter. I gotta be careful." Frank Ballard had just had a narrow escape; as he had shinnied down a wisteria vine from a third-story window, a shot from above had drilled his hat brim. Dropping a third of the distance, he wrenched his ankle and had to hobble painfully into the shadow of some rocks piled close to the house.

A few days before, Frank Ballard had put in at Newburyport. Norfolk had become too hot for safety. Four robberies in a row, but only one worth while. Now this big house, near Exeter, had paid well. The silver and jewels in the canvas bag he dragged after him would realize a sizeable amount. But he did not like these close calls. Ballard removed the black felt hat. Sticking his forefinger through the bullet hole, he muttered, "No siree. Mighta been my head. Better do the county fair in Vermont. Quieter for a while."

In the years before the War between the States, the county fair attracted people from far and near. It was held in the environs of St. Johnsbury, in a spot that was "salubrious, enhanced by mountain air and scent of clovered pasture lands," as an old handbill puts it. The fair had started after the Revolution as a cattledrovers' gathering, and the harvest festival, which took place at the same time in Montpelier, was invited to amalgamate. The combined festivity caught the imagination of the public. Crowds came from many states to enjoy the horse racing, the competitions for needlework, baking, and canning, the flower displays, the dressmaking contests, and all the other events that combined to form a week of intense activity. Every domesticated animal in the roster competed for prizes. A midway and circus acts did a roaring business. Con games, which usually break out where crowds gather, flourished. The fair and its varied attractions acted as a magnet for our four fine-feathered friends—spendthrift, miser, murderer, thief.

The first year Fat Frank Ballard honored the fair with his presence, he met Andrew Marr. A kind of wary friendship sprang up between the two men, and they laid out a campaign for the winter. During the following months, the number of crimes committed in this rich farming community rose in number and daring.

Many travelers and vagrants used the highroad from the Hudson River Valley, along the Connecticut River, and so into Canada. No one took particular notice of two affable strangers who appeared now and again in Waterford, St. Johnsbury, and smaller villages. On frosty winter nights, Fat Frank and Andrew would sit companionably around fireplaces or potbellied stoves to regale listeners with tales of adventure. They would be surveying for the government, so they said, as soon as the weather permitted.

Spring came, and summer. Again the multicolored banners at the fair fluttered against mountains and cerulean skies. Cal Longstreet, sitting on the wide verandah of a hotel in Albany, read an account of the gala opening of the fair in his morning paper. His lips curled, and his eyes narrowed in expectation. "There should be lots of beautiful women wandering about the grounds," he said to himself. "Huge crowds of them—young, fresh, buxom, dewy-eyed. I must saddle my horse for Vermont."

Somewhere along the road, near Rutland, Cal was joined by a stranger riding a bony nag. The fellow, who had seen far better days, from the look of his threadbare, much darned clothing, greeted Cal pleasantly. In an unmistakable Southern drawl, he said, "Good day. Mind if I join you for a way? This paltry bit of crowbait may founder at any jog. The best I could rustle at the moment. Truth is I've had devilish bad luck at cards lately. Lost my horse and trinkets last night. Well, better luck at the fair I trust." And Terrance Blunt shrugged his shoulders and urged his tottering steed forward.

The web, so expertly handled by the Fates, drew tighter. It would not be long now.

People of the Vermont countryside remembered vividly for years the fatal week that followed the opening of the St. Johnsbury fair. A wave of startling crimes washed over the green hills with such ferocity as to leave householders, in villages and remote farmsteads alike, starkly silent with fear. Windows were shuttered and doors barricaded as soon as darkness fell. Robberies were far-flung. Three young women, among them one Tessie Bowden, were found raped and murdered; always a thin silk scarf had been used to throttle the life out of the victim.

Fate finally pulled tight the strands of the web, on a run-down Connecticut River farm a mile or so out of Waterford. Uriah Washburn, a dour religious fanatic, was the owner of the farm. He had delusions that he was Jehovah, sent to purge the world from sin in all its horrid manifestations. His ramshackle house, seemingly never to have known a lick of paint, reared its ugly gray bulk in a grove of ragged pines and popular trees, set back from the heavily rutted road that skirted the river. Across from the house stood a huge red barn with a wide runway straight through. The center of the hipped roof supported a windowed, hexagonal cupola.

Far into the night, travelers by road, as well as farmers across the river, could see a light in the cupola. On quiet nights, the sound of hymns and prayers for deliverance from Hell caused them to shake their heads. "Uriah's crazy as an old coot," they said. "And his boy Dabby hain't no better."

But Dabby Washburn was different from his father. While Uriah let off religious fervor by song and preaching to the bats and night creatures, Dabby, a misshapen youth with a clubfoot, took pride in his "medicines." Henbane and nightshade, dock roots and sassafras, he brewed them all over a gypsy fire of sticks and walnut husks.

One stormy night, four men who had met at the St. Johnsbury fair turned up in a covered wagon at the Washburn barn. The tallest asked Uriah leave to stable his drenched pair of horses. "I'll pay you well for feed and blankets. If you can spare a few for us we would be obliged. We've driven far today and must be away early in the morning." The man took out a crocheted money pouch and chinked its contents.

Uriah eyed the pouch. He liked money as well as the next man. "Reckon yes. Can't give ye no food." He pocketed the pouch and climbed slowly to the cupola.

Dabby acted as master of ceremonies. Would the men like some of his root beer? Well, they agreed, not just their tipple, but it would do. Dabby brought blankets, and as the four men—Terrance, Frank, Cal, and Andrew—wrapped themselves in blankets and prepared to endure the hours until morning, Dabby went to a closet and filled four mugs with root beer. Deftly, so none would see, he added a dash of his brew. As the men drank, each, in turn, made some allusion to the bitter taste of the beer.

"You don't say what root you made your beer of," Terrance said, laughing.

Andrew guzzled his. "Leetle might tart. Maybe it's fermented."

"This hits the spot. I like a tang to a drink that hain't got no other kick," and Fat Frank belched and held out his mug for more.

Cal, the supercilious, drank his daintily. "I like a sweet drink. This is too bitter, by half, for me." He found a dark corner filled with straw and settled himself to sleep.

The wind had risen to wild heights, scurrying the sheets of rain among the pines and poplars, until a kind of "damnation to all sinners" weather rode the valley. According to the band of religious zealots who had converted Uriah, the millennium would be accompanied by hurricane and flood. Now Uriah, at his altar high above the roof, prayed and chanted to the wind in a thunderous voice.

Dabby dozed in a corner; then, suddenly, the henbane-nightshade brew began to work in the entrails of the four blanketed men, who had fallen into fitful sleep on the straw. Fat Frank went first; two or three screeches and his overworked heart heaved a final mighty thump. Terrance leaped from his straw bed, clutching the air wildly, vomiting his life away. Andrew just curled into a ball of anguish and soon died. But Cal Longstreet, the delicate one, crawled on his knees to the feet of Dabby and groaned, "Why—why—did you do it?"

Dabby answered, never raising a finger to help the wretched man, "Cause I know who you are. I trailed you from the fair. I saw you kill Tessie Bowden. I loved her. She was kind to me. You're none of you any good, so I got you all. God'll reward me, like Pa always says. Hear him?"

Cal sank, dying, to the fouled straw as the wind and Uriah's heaven-flung hallelujahs tore the night with clamor.

Then Dabby did the thing he felt he must. In all the local stores and taverns, he had seen handbills announcing a reward for the apprehension of the thieves who had raked such disaster across the state. The murder of Farmer Bowden's daughter had raised the temper of the countryside to fever pitch. Bring in the fiend, dead or alive. Dabby could not read, but the men who gathered in front of the posters had told him what the words meant.

Back to the closet where he kept his poisoned root beer went Dabby, full of purpose. He picked out a coil of thick rope and cut four lengths. Carefully he knotted a noose about the neck of each grotesquely sprawled body. Dabby was far stronger than most would suspect, for he had plowed deep furrows in the hilly, rock-strewn pasture of the farm ever since he was a small boy. The muscles of his long arms stood out in cords as he lifted each body to hang from the star crossbeam that divided the barn in two. In the half darkness, his squinting eyes surveyed the dead quartet. The wind had lulled; it was near morning. He flung wide the big doors at either end of the long alley between the haylofts. Stopped dead in their tracks, the reprobates now hung like four black crows. In streamed bright morning sunrays, gilding the stained corpses and lending an ironical touch to the beauty of a newborn, gentle day.

Dabby heard the sound of footsteps dragging on the narrow stairs that wound up to the cupola. With arms folded across his chest, he waited. Uriah Washburn was so wearied by his night of fighting Hell and brimstone that at first he did not see the swaying black figures hanging in a row from the star pole. It was Dabby's voice, ringing like a trumpet, that roused the man. "There they be! Four black skunks! The sheriff wanted 'em dead or alive." And the boy flung off down the path to the river.

The ugly house in the grove of pines and poplar trees is long since fallen to ruin. Tangled vines and matted weeds cover the collapsed walls. But the old Washburn barn still stands, and sometimes, in the full of the moon, four draggled black figures are seen hanging from the star pole.

It was on a September night of bright moonlight that I saw the ghosts of the tall spendthrift, the short miser, the thin murderer, and the fat thief, hanging, like flap-winged, molting cranes, in the shadowed barn. I was out walking along the roadway that passes the barn, and chanced to look through the high doors. For a space of minutes, I stood watching. Gently the forms swayed in a soft wind. The night was full of the sharp or blurred sounds so much a part of a farm country-side. But no animal of any kind stirred or whinnied or rustled among the straw, for no creature will stay in that barn.

As I took one last look before continuing along the road toward Waterford, I noticed the thing that always interests me in supernatural phenomena. Although the brightness of the moon cast rich black shadows from barrels and piled straw on the barn floor, no shadow lay under the hanging figures.

The Smuggler's Doll

AT THE END of a day in late April, 1870, when long shadows cast by the setting sun made dark, ribbonlike patterns across the streets and houses of Manhattan, an ocean liner, the Atlantic Star, out of Liverpool and Le Havre, steamed up the river to berth at a pier near Desbrosses Street. Among the persons on deck was a tall, dark, distinguished-looking woman of about thirty-five years, standing with her arm across the shoulders of a plump, fair-haired little girl, who was eagerly scanning the shores of Staten Island.

Looking through a small telescope, a kind of spyglass, the child swept the river and the distant shore. Suddenly she gurgled with pleasure. "Oh, guardie, I thaw it! I thaw it—my lovely houth," she lisped.

The woman addressed smiled down at the child and nodded. This lady had a distinctly elegant air about her. She was dressed for ocean travel in the latest fashion decreed, undoubtedly, by Worth of the Rue de la Paix. Indeed, according to Mrs. Danforth, she and her little ward, Fanchon Moncare, had only eighteen days before left Paris. After a short time in New York, required to settle some business arrangements, Mrs. Danforth would open a spacious house, of many verandahs and lace-carved cupolas, on Staten Island, where she and little Fanchon would spend the summer. Each autumn, she said, since Fanchon had become her charge, at the tender age of six, Ada Danforth had taken the child to Paris to visit her relatives.

Mrs. Danforth turned to the Englishwoman standing next to her. "It really is

47

her house," she said. "Such a fortunate little girl. I, of course, only help administer her estate—a considerable one—until she is eighteen years old."

The little girl, dressed in a cherry and white mohair dolman, smoothed the dress of the doll she carried and smiled at the English lady. Odd, thought the woman, for one so young she had a mouthful of extremely big yellow teeth.

Farther down the deck, a little scene of opposing opinions was being enacted by two of the other passengers: a Mrs. Caldwell, of Rhinebeck, New York, remarked to her husband, "I don't care what you say, Fred, there is something mighty peculiar about that pair. I sensed it the first day out. Then when I overheard a scrap of conversation between the two, I was sure of it. They are not at all what they want us to think they are."

Her husband replied wearily, "Maude, you are the limit. I haven't spoken to either of them, but I must say they look quite harmless. Just because you heard the tail end of a quarrel between them, you're all upset. That's what you get for eavesdropping."

Maude Caldwell answered tartly, "I was *not* eavesdropping. I couldn't help hearing—it took place right outside my cabin. You've heard that frizzyhaired Fanchon lisping in her ridiculous baby fashion. Well, when I heard her talking this time—something about dividing a large sum of money among four people—her voice was as raucous as a fishwife's. It was a vicious grown-up voice. I don't care how she dresses and simpers in public. There is something definitely shady, if not sinister, in that quarter. I believe our little Fanchon is many years older than she pretends, and a crook into the bargain."

A short time later, the task of warping the ship began, and plump little Fanchon Moncare ran up and down the deck, emitting trills of childish delight. When the gangplank was lowered, Fanchon, clasping her doll tightly, was first off the ship, closely followed by Mrs. Danforth.

The ritual of passing through customs, an ordeal to some people, held no fears for Fanchon. For years now, the arrival from Paris of Mrs. Danforth and her ward had been almost routine. Fanchon danced up to a customs official. "Oh, hello, Mithter Mooney. I'm back again, you thee. Would you like to give dolly and me a kith?"

Mrs. Caldwell, standing under the letter "C", watched this little charade contemptuously. "Appalling," she said. Turning to her husband, she added, "One day, that cartoon of a female will overdo it, and the exposure is something I would like to see. Well, I expect it will be on the front pages of the newspapers, so I'll keep a sharp lookout."

Fred Caldwell shook his head wearily. "Oh, Maude, let them alone. I think she's rather cute."

A customs inspector arrived at their luggage as Maude let out a blast: "Cute! Besides being revolting, I'd stake all my new Paris frocks she's forty, if she's a day."

True to form, Inspector Mooney passed the Danforth trunks and boxes through the barrier with dispatch. Ada Danforth bestowed on him one of her most ravishing smiles, and, with Fanchon skipping beside her, walked out of the pier shed. As she signaled a hansom cab, a shifty blue-chinned individual sidled up beside her. In a voice audible to her ear alone, he said, "Wing Tow's, 20 Mott Street. I'll send the bags along to Staten Island. He's waitin'."

Ada told the cabby to set them down half a block from 20 Mott Street. Later, as they rode into Chinatown, Fanchon exclaimed delightedly over the red-and-black paper signs that fluttered against the houses of the mean streets.

Then, through a dark cavern of hallway, reeking with odors of long-dead dried duck, pickled eggs, and boiled vegetables, the two mounted to a landing on the third floor. A door at Ada's right bore a painted paper banner. Gold characters on a red ground proclaimed, "Wing Hong Tow, Jades, Porcelains, Paintings."

Ada Danforth knocked on a wooden panel of the door—four short, sharp raps. After a moment, the door opened a crack and a pock-marked yellow face peered sleepily at the women. Mrs. Danforth and Fanchon entered a room in which a fog of evil odors hung like a blanket about the walls. Many times before, they had entered this anteroom. Each time, the miasma of ancient corruption was almost too much for them. But the completion of their transaction depended on the underworld channels of international jewel smugglers, of which Wing Hong Tow, once of Peking, was ruler.

Mop Gow, servant of Old Mandarin, as Wing Hong Tow was called, teetered to a heavy silk curtain covering one wall. Pulling the curtain aside, he waved Ada and Fanchon into a silk-hung cavelike room, where Wing Hong Tow awaited them.

Nodding, fluttering his long-taloned hands at them, Old Mandarin motioned to a table. Fanchon slipped her doll from the crook of her arm and took a thin, sharp-bladed knife from her purse. Laying the doll on a table under a sputtering gas jet, she gutted the stuffed body with one flick of her hand. Among the shreds of sawdust spilling out on the table were half a hundred unset jewels, some superbly faceted, others smoothly polished. For a moment, the three were silent. A hummingbird fluttered frantically in a jade-and-gold filigree cage hanging at Old Mandarin's elbow. Then Fanchon Moncare spoke. Gone was the lisp; she had suddenly rid herself of all her infantilism. In place of the wide-eyed child, a strident, crafty jewel thief appeared.

"Now, take a look at that!" she said. "The best haul I've had in years! Look at these rubies—pigeon-blood, no less—and these here emeralds. Right out of a blinkin' rajah's breastplate—all ceremonial stuff. Look here." She separated fifteen or twenty faceted diamonds of varying sizes from the welter of shimmering color. "I robbed a French countess at Mentone. This was a necklace I broke up." She stood back and grinned.

Old Mandarin grinned. "Good, good," he said, in a thin, whining voice. "But where is remaining stones in necklace? Only few here. Where?" The voice quavered to a stop, but the eyes, no more than puckers of skin in the moon-shaped old face, looked intently at Fanchon.

Ada, wiser than Fanchon, who had guttersnipe avarice, said sharply, "I told you he'd suspect. Give them over. Let's settle this and get out of here. You know how I loathe it all."

A black look came over Fanchon's puffy face, and she plunged her hand into the neck of her bodice. Out came a sweaty chamois bag, which she threw on the table.

Carefully opening the bag, Old Mandarin emptied the diamonds onto the board and nodded like a satisfied Buddha. He spoke to Mop Gow, who was half asleep in the folds of a wall curtain. "Bring money satchel—quick."

The room was well soundproofed by the thick wall draperies, and this was fortunate, for thereafter the sounds of haggling over price between Old Mandarin and Fanchon increased in volume until Ada Danforth, handkerchief pressed to her nose, hurried from the room to wait in the hall.

For half an hour, the voices rose and fell. Ada could, now and again, distinguish Fanchon's. "Don't you threaten me, you old snake! Baby Fanchon's the best bet you've got. Walk off the boat I do, every time, right under the noses of those customs fools. A quarter of a million in safe jewels in my doll's guts. No, you won't hurt me, *nor* Ada. With her grand airs, she's just as valuable as I am. Now, come on, give me a price!"

At last, when Ada was wondering if the session would never end, Fanchon came out. Red of face, bosom heaving, she yelled, "God-damned old dragon! For two cents, I'd slit him the way I do the doll. Come on, I need a drink."

However closely Mrs. Caldwell, at her Rhinebeck mansion, scanned the daily newspapers, she did not immediately see anything about the apprehending of a crook named Fanchon Moncare. For once again, with police in half the capitals of Europe working with the New York police, Baby Fanchon had pulled off a beautiful coup. She and Ada had, between them, realized nearly a hundred and fifteen thousand dollars. True enough, two members of Boss Tweed's ring expected a 'donation' for silence, and Mayor Oakley Hall, who with well-publicized charities, fostered Tweed's popularity among the poor, would receive a handsome present. Still, as in past years, the 'take' from this Parisian excursion by the two ladies from Staten Island was extremely big.

Fanchon, who while at work acted the part of childhood innocence, on her time off whored with the lowest sort of companions. The Bowery saloons knew her. Rockaway Park and the race tracks were enlivened by her presence. Donning a black wig for these jubilations, she dressed in the height of vulgar style. Ada Danforth, always impeccably turned out, was horrified and did not join Fanchon in her junketing. Her role of doting guardian to dear rich little Fanchon Moncare, whether on European pleasure trips or parties on the green lawns of her 'estate,' was not so easily dropped.

One day, Fanchon, calling herself Estelle Ridley, arrived at Rockaway Park in the entourage of Dart Crawley, one of Tweed's henchmen. He was a shyster lawyer, a cardsharp, and a pimp of the first water. He was, as well, getting extremely tired of Estelle Ridley. Not only did he know enough about the woman to hang her higher than Haman, but she annoyed him with her childish tricks.

Selecting from his bevy of satellites an unsavory character, Martin Gaynor, Crawley told him to lay conquest to the heart and thighs of Estelle Ridley. But Destiny, a little out of breath, hurriedly approached Miss Ridley and pushed

Gaynor aside. One day, at Rockaway Park race track, Gaynor, half-drunk, introduced Estelle Ridley to Magda Hamilton, a harpy with an inordinate absorption in money.

Soon after the meeting, Estelle resumed her disguise of Fanchon to pull off a job in Chicago. Only once before had Fanchon attempted a jewel robbery in this country. Ada Danforth had repeatedly cautioned her against it. "After all," warned Ada, "you are unique in still being able to impersonate a child of ten or twelve, simply because you are a midget. You are liked by the customs men; they would no more believe that you smuggled thousands of dollars' worth of diamonds in that ridiculous doll than that their own children would. For God's sake, don't get notions. Let some mug of Tweed's do this job. Besides it's nearly time for us to take another European trip."

The two women quarreled, and Fanchon set out for Chicago with her new crony, Magda Hamilton. The job consisted first of attracting the attention of an old millionaire, Rufus Twombly. Fanchon handled it with consummate skill. The old man was a widower, with a huge house in Lake Forest. Years before, his only daughter, a child of fourteen, had died. In this—to his fond mind—engaging child, he saw a replica of his little Elsie. It was not long before Magda, now in the role of Ada Danforth, and Fanchon were ensconced in Rufus Twombly's mansion. The rest was simple. Give the servants a day off, doctor the old boy's coffee, rifle the wall safe in his bedroom, and escape into the dark woods that surrounded the house, there to be picked up by a barouche and team of fast horses.

All went according to plan, but when the loot, amounting to several hundred thousand dollars, was to be divided, behind shuttered windows in the Staten Island house, things went wrong. The recriminations between Fanchon and Old Mandarin in the fusty silken cave on Mott Street were mild as an Epworth League social compared to what took place between Fanchon and her new accomplice.

Finally, Fanchon shrieked, "Never again, you bloody twister! You get what I choose to give you—five thousand dollars! You can stick it, you bitch!"

There was an ominous silence; then Magda answered, so low that Fanchon had to crane her short neck to hear, "Stick it, huh? That's just what I'll do. But where I'll stick it will be the end of you."

The next morning, Fanchon, arrayed in baby-blue silk and pink rosebuds, with her beloved doll clutched tightly in her arms, walked up the gangplank of the Atlantic steamer Panonia, accompanied by her guardian, Mrs. Danforth, for a trip to Europe.

The travelers went first to Biarritz and, a few weeks later, to San Sebastian. Then, one night in Marseilles, the Vicomte de Point Talliere was robbed as he was leaving the opera. Everyone knew that the doddering old man habitually wore a fortune in jewels with evening dress and carried another fortune, in francs, on his person. There had been a spate of robberies at about that time, but this one differed tragically from the others; the Vicomte, who was very old, had been dealt a blow during the robbery, and he died on the way to his hotel.

Murder! The apache who performed the deed was hastily paid off. In a few days, cutting their visit short, Mrs. Danforth and little Fanchon Moncare booked passage for America. Ada told acquaintances, "Poor little Fanchon has been taken ill. I am terribly worried, and I do not trust French doctors. We must get home to our family physician."

When the ship reached New York, smiling Mrs. Danforth and bubbling Fanchon, doll clasped tightly, again stood at the rail of the incoming Atlantic Star. This time, however, the dockside atmosphere was tense. Two groups of men stood waiting at the pier. As soon as the gangplank was lowered, each group took a stand by the customs barriers.

Fanchon, always in the lead, was halfway down the gangplank before she became aware of the eyes gazing up at her. She stopped in her tracks, but people eager to get off the boat pushed her and Ada, who was right behind her, and they were compelled to continue. A man came up to them and said, "Miss Moncare, alias Ridley, I arrest you—." Fanchon hurled her doll over the dock-side into the oily water of the river, and, screaming obscenities, fought like a tiger as four men attempted to subdue her. Through all this Mrs. Danforth stood, cool and collected, gazing at the horrid exhibition. Finally, she and Fanchon were escorted to a Black Maria waiting just outside the pier entrance.

The next morning at breakfast, Mrs. Caldwell, in Rhinebeck, spread the New York *Herald* wide in front of her. "Fred, here it is, bold as brass—the whole affair. Don't stop me. I will read it to you, every word." Maude cleared her throat.

The gist of the report was this: An arrest had been made that would lead to the smashing by New York and foreign police of one of the most powerful groups of jewel smugglers ever encountered by the authorities. A scandal of mounting proportions would break as soon as evidence could be sifted. This concerned the Boss Tweed ring. The prisoner, a woman midget who called herself Fanchon Moncaré, or Estelle Ridley, had for years posed as a child, making annual trips to France accompanied by a woman accomplice named Ada Danforth. These journeys of child and guardian resulted in robberies of wealthy persons, usually gullible elderly men or women. In some cases, aging beaux became infatuated with the beautiful Mrs. Danforth. Sometimes the victim fell prey to Fanchon's childish antics. After the robberies, the jewels, pried from their settings, were concealed in the sawdust body of Fanchon's doll. The two women had taken particular pains, over the years, to ingratiate themselves with the customs officials. Detection of the smugglers had been possible through a report made by a heavily veiled woman, who gave police the details and advised them of the arrival of the women on the Atlantic Star.

As Maude Caldwell put her paper down, she found her husband sitting bolt upright in his chair. "Maude," he said sternly, "did you, heavily veiled, go to the police about this woman? Did you?"

Maude Caldwell laughed. "No, silly, I did not. How would I know any of the details about either of them? It was simply a hunch. If I ever saw a criminal on the prowl, it was that smirking, lisping, fish-eyed dwarf."

The trial of Fanchon Moncare and Ada Danforth was a sensation in police annals. The reverberations, which affected men prominent in politics, were damaging and far-reaching. Graft was uncovered involving high-ups in the Tweed ring and customs men of the Port of New York. Fanchon, who proved to be forty-six, was sentenced to life imprisonment. Ada Danforth, thirty-six, was sent up as accessory for twenty years.

A few weeks after the two women were imprisoned, the Staten Island house, with its white balustraded widow's walk and sloping green lawns, where Fanchon had played cutthroat croquet, was sold. The buyer was a veiled woman leaning on the arm of a rapscallion-appearing man of immense frame. The deed was made out to Mrs. Dartway Crawley. The informer Magda Hamilton had apparently feathered her nest and secured for herself a very appropriate husband.

Years passed. Boss Tweed had been extradited from Spain and had died in prison. Tammany Hall had suffered all manner of political fluctuations. One

morning, there appeared in the newspaper a small item: "Mrs. Ada Danfor
would welcome ladies of highest social standing to Fifth Avenue dressmaki
atelier. Only latest French mode is shown to customers."

Few persons connected this dignified name with one made famous in a noto
ous case, called the "smuggler's doll," of two decades ago. Forgotten complet
behind iron bars, was Fanchon Moncare. Even when she died, a few months aft
the release of Ada Danforth, no mention of it appeared in the newspapers.

One night, Magda Hamilton, unable to sleep, turned restlessly in her be
Long ago, Crawley had left her and gone to California to prospect. Sudder
the woman sat rigid, clutching the bedclothes to her throat. A figure was a
proaching—a well-known figure, in pink and white. Dressed like a child, f;
whey-faced, it was really an old woman, almost deformed. In her hand, pois
as one does a dagger, the hag held a doll, its china head down. Magda shrieke
then gurgled as the head of the doll was rammed down her throat.

Magda was discovered the following morning; blood had run out of bo
corners of her gaping mouth. A medical examiner reported that the woman h;
died from strangulation; the membrane of her throat was torn, as if a hea'
object had been rammed down it with great violence; the jaws were lock
wide open. The murder weapon was not found.

Real-estate men said the Crawley place was a jinx to rent. No one wou
stay in it for more than a few weeks, sometimes only for days. Ghosts? Perhap
Tenants told of being awakened at night by a sound like low cursing, followe
by strident chattering and the appearance of a short, squat woman, in a chilc
pink-and-white frock, walking through the rooms. In one outstretched hand sl
carried what appeared to be a rag doll with a china head. The object dripp
with blood. The apparition bore the doll as one would a dagger.

Often reports have come in to New York Harbor authorities, particular
during World War II, of a feminine figure parading the widow's walk atop th
roof of the old Crawley place, on Staten Island. She pauses, leveling a telescop
Always she seems to be interested in ship movements off Sandy Hook. Some sa
it is a woman. Others say it is a child who clasps a doll under her arm.

Frieze of Pomegranates
and Phoenix Birds

PAYNTON HALL, GLOUCESTER COUNTY, VIRGINIA, 1745

THIS IS a story of luxury, depravity, and revenge, with the central figure a woman who stopped at nothing to gain her ends, who lived by sham, trickery, and dark desires, her every emotion a lie. Yet she, who was the cause of four deaths by violence, died in her rose-bower bed, supposedly from natural causes.

The husband, Fairfax Dalton, had built himself a substantial, beautifully appointed house on a reach of the York River where it widens almost to the spaciousness of a bay. He called his house Paynton Hall. He married Lettitia Brundage, and thereafter life became a series of violent tantrums and quarrels incited for the flimsiest of reasons. Eventually, he sought peace in frequent visits to Rosewell, the home of his neighbors the Pages, where it seemed to him he stepped from Purgatory into Paradise. Mann Page II and his beautiful wife, Anne Corbin Tayloe, of Mount Airy, always welcomed their friend warmly. Many of the entertainments that were the very keystone of Virginia hospitality were arranged by Anne to banish some particularly unpleasant marital encounter from the mind of Fairfax.

In my admiration for Rosewell, I yield to no house in America. The late Thomas Tileston Waterman, authority on Virginia houses of three centuries, called Rosewell "the largest and finest of American houses of the Colonial period."

57

Though my knowledge of this style of house is in no way as complete as Mr. Waterman's, I regard Rosewell as the finest house in Palladian style I have ever seen in this country. I would rather own it, ruinous as it stands, than any other in the United States.

Miranda Barstow-Bellamy, just arrived from Charlottesville, tapped her cheek with her fan and said, "A ball at Rosewell, my dear Angela? How diverting! Moonlight, roses, and gallantry. At least, I expect we may count on moonlight."

Her hostess, Mrs. Farrell, of Woodbridge Hall near Whitemarsh, laughed. "If this weather holds for two more nights, the moon should be at the full. Anne Page always seems to have most prodigious good fortune whenever she gives a ball. I, for one, am on tenterhooks of excitement. I love that house so. Rosewell is the essence of romance. Moonlight, roses, delicious French wines, handsome officers." She sighed. "Now, let me hear the latest gossip."

Mrs. Barstow-Bellamy, buxom dowager, eagerly gave it. "I admit I was vastly surprised, even shocked, to hear that Lettitia Dalton intends to be present at the ball, so soon after the mysterious death of her sister. What do you suppose is the truth of the matter? Such conflicting reports. I heard from Dell Prescott that Melanie Dulaney had point-blank accused Lettitia of causing Caro's death by sending her out to the hothouse in that terrible storm—for grapes, of all things. The hothouse was being repaired, and in the darkness Caro ran into some scaffolding. The glass collapsed and cut her so badly she died of severed veins. An old black man found her there in the morning."

Mrs. Farrell shook her head. "I heard differently. I heard from my handmaid Bet that when Caro returned to Paynton last week, she and Lettitia had a dreadful, screaming quarrel over that Dabney boy Caro was so in love with. He *is* a young rake, but no worse than most. Lettitia threatened to send her sister back to Bolt Hall. Then, in that *volte-face* of mood in which Lettitia excels, she had a 'turn' and begged Caro to get her the grapes. In the storm, a rotted tree branch fell and crushed Caro's skull. It all sounds as melodramatic as the rest of Lettitia Dalton's tantrums. A terrible woman, really. I was fond of Caro. And that poor foolish husband of Lettitia's is breaking under it."

"I was fond of Caro, too," Mrs. Barstow-Bellamy said. "Lettitia is devoid of feeling, of course. Once she sets her mind to arriving late at a ball, to stun the countryside with her toilette and fancied importance, it takes more than the death of a sister to cancel it." She paused, then said, "What shall you wear, Angela? I have brought bronze satin draped in gold lace."

Angela Farrell lifted her voice so that her husband, who was approaching, would hear. "I shall content myself with that old red taffeta. I cannot persuade my husband that I need another gown before the Governor's Birthday Ball."

Her husband joined them, smiling. "Nor will you, with all your wiles. Extravagance is your familiar, you witch. We set off tomorrow for Whitemarsh. I've arranged to stop over for the ball at Quennel's Tavern. We shall be well housed." Turning to Mrs. Barstow-Bellamy, he said, "Mistress Miranda, what do you make of Lettitia going to a ball two days after her sister's death?"

Mrs. Barstow-Bellamy shook her head. "I'm going to the ball to have a good time, and Lettitia's presence is not going to spoil it for me," she said.

When Rosewell, a spacious red-brick house, was left to Mann Page II by his father, he was the proudest man in Gloucester County. Robert Carter, known as King Carter, of Corotoman, had built a series of splendid country mansions in Virginia—Sabine Hall, Berkeley, Nomini Hall, Cleve, and Rosewell, the last in 1726. Rosewell became a showplace, and many a coach was driven over the vile roads to see it.

Soon after Mann Page II settled in, he realized that his heritage was not complete. For one thing, a drawing in the breakfast chamber showed that Corinthian-capped pilasters, which were proposed to enrich the arches of the stair hall and flank the doors, had not been set in place. This was one of the first tasks he undertook. It is said that no man despises his heritage. Mann Page II delighted in his. A short time later, he proposed to, and married, one of the handsomest women in Virginia, and elevated Rosewell to a plane of hospitality comparable to that of Corotoman, the house of his grandfather King Carter. Friends came to Rosewell to visit for a day, a night, or as long as they wished to stay. Since the York River and Carter's Creek washed Rosewell on three sides, Page received his guests by water. He would then conduct them through his famed box maze. The rose gardens regaled all viewers; tapestries of flowers in variegated colors spread wide around the garden fountains.

The plan of Rosewell was that of a high, square central block of five stories.

A pitched roof supported massive chimneys and twin gazebos. From the lantern windows, one was treated to a superb panorama of meadowland, low hills, and the misty reaches of York River and Carter's Creek. Two one-story quadrant connections (the Palladian demilune) joined the pavilions that projected from the east and west façades to a pair of dependencies. Each of these amounted to a good-sized house of one and a half stories, embracing five dormer windows across the roof. The interior plan of Rosewell showed five large rooms on the first floor. On the second was a huge apartment used as a ballroom. The stair well, most noteworthy detail of the house, was immensely high. Extending from the first floor to the rooftop, the sweep of richly carved balustrade carried to the lunettes in the arched lantern supporting the outlook gazebos.

True to the prediction of Mrs. Barstow-Bellamy, a polished-silver moon hung high on the night of Anne Page's ball. June had been lavish with roses. Tall rose trees, bushes, and climbing vines showed bud and full flower in perfection. Casks and magnums of rare French wines had arrived by ship in Chesapeake Bay a few days before. The consignment to Mann Page II was loaded on plantation flatboats and poled up the York River. The cook, Mammy Zoë, with an army of helpers, had spent days baking, roasting, and assembling all manner of delectable viands to be placed on the flower-garlanded circular buffets.

Guests who were staying in the house began arriving by midafternoon, exclaiming over the beauty of the decorations. There were flowers everywhere, with roses of legion variety and all conceits of arrangement. At candlelight, most of the three hundred-odd guests had arrived. Battalions of French wax tapers sputtered in crystal and bronze-doré sconces and chandeliers. The odor of perfumed wax softly permeated the damask-hung rooms. Mann Page and his wife went from room to room, welcoming their guests.

"Where is Lettitia?" Anne asked Fairfax Dalton.

"Upstairs," he answered, looking embarrassed.

Doremus, the Pages' gigantic black butler, watched his master anxiously. The buffet was ready and waiting. Wine was passed around. Conversation became staccato. Then, just when Mann was about to signal Doremus to announce supper, Lettitia Dalton appeared at the head of the staircase. Tiny in stature almost to deformity, she held her head regally, and her eyes, as always, cast a disdainful look over the assembled planters and their wives and daughters. She had usurped the rose scheme of Rosewell. Wide hoops distended her gown of rose-pink satin. Panniers of rose-latticed lace almost submerged the childlike figure. Her powdered hair was massed with roses and plumes of rose color in the Versailles style, which had not yet become prevalent in the Colonies.

Without a word of greeting, a smile, or a wave of the hand to Anne or Mann Page, Lettitia slowly descended the stairs. As her husband mounted a few steps to meet her, she said something sharply out of the corner of her heavily rouged mouth. He blushed and stepped back, letting his flamboyant wife continue on the progress she had so carefully timed.

Lettitia then greeted some of the guests indifferently, nodded to Anne Page, and sailed into the dining room. Officially, to Lettitia's mind, the ball at Rosewell had opened.

Some time before midnight, when the ball was in full sway, Lettitia Dalton signaled Fairfax to call their coach. During the drive to Paynton Hall, she was sulky. "I hate that Anne Page, with her roses. Roses are *my* flower. But I topped them all tonight. I even drew admiration from that Englishman Godfrey Chandos. I hear he's a captain, and heir to a dukedom."

The next morning, Fairfax went to his wife's boudoir, the finest room at Paynton. The room always stifled him with its elaborate trappings of rose-pink swags and furbelows. Roses, roses, everlastingly roses! The scent, the touch, even the taste of rose petals in jellies and condiments.

"It was a good ball, wasn't it, my dear? All seemed to go off well." Fairfax packed a kiss on the back of his wife's plump white hand. She withdrew her hand angrily.

"No, it was not. Those frumps of planters' wives. Dowdy beyond words. That Tripp girl ogling all the young men, even Captain Chandos." She paused, then added haughtily, "*He* has been to Versailles, and he complimented me on the elegance of my coiffure."

As Fairfax walked towards the door, Lettitia said, "I shall give a ball for the Captain soon."

Fairfax turned back. "Not in this house," he said. "It was bad enough that you went to the Pages' practically on the day your sister was buried. You will give no ball until I say so. This is *my* house, remember." He left the room.

A feline purr followed Fairfax's retreating back, like a wisp of silk, sibilant among the rose cushions. "Yes, it is your house—for a while," Lettitia whispered. "I can get rid of you as easily as I did of Caro."

The eyes of Lettitia of Paynton closed, but she did not sleep. Instead, she let her thoughts drift back to the quarrel with Caro—how she had noticed the girl plucking distractedly at a bunch of hothouse grapes. A storm had been brewing; high wind from off the bay swept inland. Branches of trees, big limbs, were wrenched from the oaks and walnut trees in the park. The glass house, she knew, was in process of repair; she had seen piles of glass panes perched on the roof beams. Dismissing Caro, she had thrown a hooded cloak about her and hurried out. Carefully she had piled shards of glass above a spot where the finest grapes hung in clusters. The roof was shored up by rickety planks, and she had wrenched the planks askew. Then, putting a loose board in such a position that anyone stumbling over it would send the shoring clattering, she had returned to her room. Later in the evening, when the wind was shrieking at its worst, she had begged Caro to go to the glass house and fetch her a basket of grapes. The morning had told the success of her plan. Now she had only to think of an equally effective one for Fairfax.

Caro Brundage had been dead a month when, one evening, Fairfax returned from Rosewell. He called out for his brother Colville, who was staying with them, but there was no response. Lettitia, he suspected, was dining in her room. Let her be. After a meal alone, he went up the stairs to bed. As always, when the moon was bright, he paused for a moment on the landing to admire the tracery of light and shadow picked out by rays shining through the lantern windows. The design of pomegranates and phoenix birds of the richly modeled cornice seemed never so fluid as in this light. "Marvelous," he murmured, and went to his room.

Shortly afterward, he heard the sound of someone calling his name from the stair well. "Fairfax. Fairfax. Here, Fairfax. I am here." It was the faintest kind of sound. Odd, he thought, who could it be? He listened. It came again. "Fairfax! Here—please." He detected a note of fear, of urgency. But it was no voice he recognized.

Opening the door, he went out onto the balcony that ran along two sides of the wall. The lower hall was in deep shadow. It came again, this time on a rising note. "Quick, Fairfax! Here I am. Look over, see."

Instinctively, he grasped the balustrades in both hands. Leaning his weight against the spindles, he peered down. There was a sound of rending wood. The man grasped at air, as, with a frantic cry, he hurtled head downward to the marble floor below.

Cadmus, an old servant, summoned Colville Dalton from the stables, where he had just unsaddled his horse. Colville found the dead body of his brother lying in the hall, the face a bloody pulp, the neck broken. Splintered bits of the walnut balustrade were scattered about the floor. When a search was made of the house for anyone who had witnessed the accident, none was found. The house servants slept in a brick dormitory at the end of the kitchen garden. Clairy, Lettitia's hand-maid, said she had been sent by her mistress on an errand to the overseer's house, a mile away.

Colville approached his sister-in-law's bedchamber. The door was locked. Softly he called to her. Sleepy-eyed, Lettitia, clad in night clothes, opened the door a crack. No, she had heard nothing. She had taken a sleeping potion for her migraine. "No!" she said impatiently. "I tell you I heard nothing. Now, go. Let me sleep. Have you no pity?" She slammed the door in his face.

Whatever his suspicions may have been, Colville Dalton left Paynton Hall without verifying them. Perhaps he knew that nothing he could do would ever convict so accomplished a liar and intrigante as his sister-in-law. Fairfax was a heavy man; the spindles, lightly spun, were weakened by carving. It was the kind of accident that often happened. There had been no witness.

The countryside was shocked by the horror of Fairfax Dalton's death. Openly, no one dared accuse Lettitia. Clairy said she had given her mistress the usual strong doses of sleeping potion; she was asleep when she left on her errand. But the rumblings of doubt still persisted. Colville spent the winter at Rosewell with the Mann Pages. In the spring, he sailed for England.

Lettitia visited Rivanna. Bolt Hall, where she had been born, was much the same. Sitting on the terrace overhanging the river, she corralled her life in memory. There were gaps in her family history, and she had told Fairfax Dalton a long tale of mixed truths when he had paid court to her. Her father was Boult—or Bolt, as she preferred to call it. She knew that he had come to Albermarle County in 1660, a young emigrant from the Duchy of Brunswick, and had lived at Bolt Hall. He had had four wives, of which Lettitia's mother was the last. How Caro and she had got the name of Brundage she did not know. In all ways, the family and its background were mysterious. She shrugged off her memories and resigned herself to a solitary stay in Bolt Hall.

A few months after Fairfax's death Lettitia's heavy traveling coach returned to Paynton. Now she was prepared to start her campaign to ensnare the handsome British Captain. It was June, the rose month. She would give a rose ball.

But the coronet of duchess was never to adorn the head of the murderess from Rivanna. One night her supposed migraine returned *in extremis*. She died before morning.

Before Lettitia died, she had been the cause of two more deaths. One was that of Tacton, son of Cadmus and coachman to the Dalton family. Lettitia, although she had not ridden since she was a girl, kept a few Thoroughbred saddle horses at Paynton Hall. One day, a mare Lettitia had chosen to present to a friend, ran off into the swampland, near the river. When Tacton told Cadmus about it, he, in turn, told his mistress. Although the spring rains had set in, making the surrounding river meadows a quagmire, Lettitia insisted that Tacton search immediately for the mare. He returned to Paynton Hall later, saying he had sighted the mare; she was on a small sandbar almost surrounded by quicksand bogs. Lettitia ordered the slave to bring the mare in without delay. He left to obey, and no more was ever seen of mare or Tacton again.

The second death was that of Clairy's daughter Clairisse. Greedy for strong slaves to work the fields, Lettitia had frequently ordered girls to the stud cabin who were too young even to conceive. Clairisse was one of them, and she died from the brutality of the raping she received. Later the circumstances of Lettitia's death gave rise to the story that Clairy had poisoned her mistress to avenge Clairisse's death. The story has never been substantiated or disproved. The fact remains that, whether it happened by nature's hand or Clairy's, Lettitia's days on earth were finished.

Some time after Colville Dalton had inherited his brother's estate and gone back to live at Paynton Hall, the details of Caro's death leaped into the glare of discovery. On her deathbed, an old German woman, Hilda Kloch, who had brought Asa Boult's sister from the Duchy of Brunswick and then remained to live at Bolt Hall, told the following:

Lettitia's mother, who was common-law wife to Asa Boult, had taken the marriage name, Brundage, of Asa's sister. Caro, daughter of the Brundages, was reared at Bolt Hall; she was not Lettitia's sister.

Caro had been got with child by the Dabney boy while she was staying at Paynton. Terrified at what her supposed sister would do, she had run back to old Hilda, at Bolt Hall, and there, eventually, she had given birth to a child, a boy.

Soon afterward, a man, doubtless in the pay of Lettitia, appeared at Bolt Hall. He said he was from the Dabneys, who demanded the child. The two women fought him, one with little strength, the German woman like a mad being, but he overpowered them and escaped down the river with the child. The scene that ensued between Caro and Lettitia, when Caro went back to Paynton and begged for the return of her baby, signed her death warrant. No one seems to be able to shed any light on what happened to the baby.

A Virginia woman who lived at Shelly, one of the Page houses, not far from Rosewell, kept a remarkable journal of daily events. Among other things, the journal includes some brilliant water-color sketches of the impressive and handsome table tombs of the Page family, which dream away the decades in a family cemetery to the east of Rosewell. The woman refers often to houses in the vicinity of Shelly and Rosewell. Of Paynton, she says, "A terrible cry rings through the houses at night." She speaks of "blood on the marble, impossible to rub clean." Doubtless this is the spectral enactment of Fairfax Dalton's plunge down the stair well after the treachery of Lettitia.

A man in Charlottesville told me that his grandmother used to go to parties at Paynton Hall in the time of Colville's son, around 1838. She remembered hearing that the passages and rooms were all kept brightly lighted, for a number of accidents, or near accidents, had occurred in dark and ill-lit hallways. Some said they had seen a small shadowy figure of a woman passing through the halls. As she went by, they had felt a sudden push, or a tripping of their feet. One lady had only saved herself from hurtling down the stairs by grasping a newel post.

In 1840, it was reported, slaves refused to stay in the huts near the old stud cabin, saying they had seen a Negro woman, crouched on the floor of the cabin —wailing over a young girl covered with blood. The superintendent told of hearing sobs of terrible anguish coming from the cabin at night. The ghost of poor Clairy had returned to discover the violation of her young daughter.

Paynton Hall was burned to the ground during the battle of York Plains Ford. Nothing but grass-grown foundations remain. Rosewell, gutted by fire in 1916, still stands to the elements, in ravaged beauty. Tough sour grass and nettles break like waves against the rose-red brick foundations, while the pale-amber and faintly mauve glass panes remind the visitor of how superbly appointed the house once was. And what stories one hears of hauntings! From all sorts of persons come tales of linkboys standing beside the great pedimented doorway at night, lighting Colonial governors, as well as Dandridge Randolph, Spottiswood, and Dulaney belles, into the Corinthian pilastered stair well. Violin and harpsichord music is said to issue from the house, and the figure of a woman in a red cloak runs toward the grove where the flower gardens once bloomed. An assignation? A young officer and a Virginia belle? Certainly tremendous doings took place within the fire-riven walls of Rosewell. All I hear seems in keeping with the magnificence and stature of this barren, deserted house.

Death of a Great Heart

Trouble Maker

MARYLAND HUNT CUP COURSE, MARYLAND, 1935

*This story is dedicated to the memory of Trouble Maker, an outstanding
Thoroughbred, one of the greatest horses ever raced in America.*

RECORD CROWD out today," I heard a voice at my elbow say. Turning, I greeted the Master of Rose Tree Hunt. "It is surely," I answered. "And a grand day for the race. I came down from New York to see Trouble Maker win. He should, you know. He has everything to do it with. And what heart that animal has! One day, given luck, he will win the Grand National." But the god Mercury, patron of horses and racehorses, withheld his glance that day. It was a fine cool day—splendid racing weather. A colorful crowd of steeplechase devotees milled around the paddock at the Maryland Hunt Cup Course. There were the usual invitations to wet one's whistle, and dates were made to meet and dine after the race. Good-natured banter was tossed back and forth among the crowd.

The first races on the card were run with no show of exceptional prowess. Then came the big event of the day, the Maryland Hunt Cup. The field came in, a fine-looking lot of horses—rangy, in the pink of condition. I looked for the dark-brown gelding ridden by Noel Laing—Trouble Maker, by Berrilldon out

69

of The Busybody by Meddler. Then I saw him, loping along—a heartwarming sight, for he was the classic type of chaser. His easy stride, beautifully fluid way of moving and—I knew from having seen him perform before—eagerness at the fences, proclaimed champion.

Today, Trouble Maker would need every ounce of speed, lifting power and stamina he possessed. Timber was spread across the course with a vengeance. Just as the jumps, brush and water, at Aintree are world-known for hazards, so the timber fences at the Maryland Cup Course are known at the most formidable of their kind. A horse must be a versatile timber topper to cover this course without grief.

The sun shone on the French blue, old rose, and silver of the silks of Mrs. Sommerville, owner of Trouble Maker, as the horses maneuvered for place at the starting post. The crowd was so silent I could hear crows cawing in the oak trees at one side of the course.

"They're off!"—that magic shout at a race meeting—and the onlookers settled down for a few moments of rigid intentness. Every eye followed the field. At first, the horses were bunched. Then the slower ones began to lag, as the bid for place was made. Trouble Maker, I could see, was lying well out of the ruck, going carefully and breathing easily.

The sun picked out the brilliant colors of silks, enabling one to follow with the naked eye the varying positions of the riders in the race. I had my long-range glasses and could distinguish practically every hair in a braided tail on the farthest reach. A slight rise occurs as the horses approach the sixteenth fence on this course; then, as they settle down for the run to the seventeenth, the devil of all timber jumps, there is a slight dip.

As the field approached this timber, I was conscious that Trouble Maker seemed to sway a bit, although in the main he was running a superbly even race. Beautiful handling by Laing helped Trouble Maker to gauge his fences in uncommon style. The horse wared his takeoff and never pecked once on landing. Now the seventeenth fence loomed as high as a paddock gate. I saw Trouble Maker gather all his forces and make his bid to win. Many other watchers saw this, as well; there was a breathless hush across the acres of grass. Up rose the horses. Up, up—they seemed to fly upwards—then came a crash, the sound of iron hitting timber. Trouble Maker hit the top rail of the seventeenth fence. He crashed down in a heap of flailing hoofs, breaking his neck.

Hotspur won the Maryland Hunt Cup that day, well and ably. Captain Kettle was second, Gigolo and Outlaw third and fourth. A memorable finish. But in the hearts of the watchers it was Trouble Maker's race, a game race run by a horse of surpassing greatness of heart. He was buried where he fell, in front of the seventeenth fence of timber rails on the Maryland Cup Course.

A young man who lives not far from this course told me that one night he had been to call upon a girl who lived a few miles away. Shortly after midnight, as he was driving home, he looked out across the fields where the race is annually run. To his surprise, he saw a horse standing near a timber fence. He stopped the car and got out to investigate. As he walked across the fields, he realized he was approaching the seventeenth jump. There, in front of the timber, stood a big brown horse calmly cropping grass. Stealthily the young man approached the spot. Then, to his dismay, he realized that he could see right through the animal to the timber rails beyond. The apparition threw back its head, whinnied, and ran off, disappearing down the field.

A well-known head stableman gave me a report of his meeting (personal encounters are legion) with the active ghost of Trouble Maker. It seems this man had heard many tales about the reappearance of the great horse at the seventeenth fence on the course. One night, finding himself in the vicinity, he walked over to the much discussed spot. When he was within two hundred yards or so of the place where Trouble Maker fell, he saw a horse frolicking about on the grass.

The man told me, "I wasn't really surprised to see the horse. But he was frisky as a colt. I said to him, 'Now, look here, Trouble Maker, I know all about you. You've suffered a broken neck, you're no yearling. You were foaled in 1923. You fell in 1935. My boy, you're twelve years old! But if you'd had the luck you should, you could have jumped rings around any other horse a lot later than twelve years. So may the gods bless you, whatever you are.'"

In answer, the equine apparition circled the timber, gave ware to his takeoff, and leaped the rails like a stag.

There, by the seventeenth fence, they buried Maker. But he considers he is a pensioner, having won his ease and the unalterable right to run the Maryland Cup whenever he sees fit. May he long enjoy it.

Buried in Crystal

A YOUNG GIRL in a brown silk dress walked slowly along California Street, in San Francisco, twirling her parasol. From the crown of her yellow, rose-clustered bonnet to the tips of her fawn *glacé*-kid boots, she was a plump young fashion plate, evoking the *ateliers de la mode* of Paris. But the girl idling along the sunny street was not French. One sensed instantly she came of sturdy American stock. Only her elaborate clothes and movements, in "the Grecian bend," spoke of French salons.

The girl, Flora Sommerton, and her parents were straight out of Kansas City, Kansas. Her father, Charles Benbow Sommerton, was one of the richest of the nabobs of Nob Hill.

Flora had gone out, ostensibly, to while away the time before she was to take a nap, her "beauty sleep." "You must nap three hours, Flora, at least—and *sleep*, not just close your eyes," her mother had admonished her when, just after luncheon, Flora said she was going out.

The Sommerton mansion, a Sultan's dyspeptic dream in gray and muddy-brown stone, was in a state of pandemonium; at ten o'clock that night Flora, her parents, and her Aunt Helene, of the grand airs, were to stand at the first rise of the marble staircase to receive hundreds of guests. It was Flora's eighteenth birthday, and she was making her début in San Francisco society.

However at peace with her fashionable world Flora appeared, she was, in

73

truth, seething with excitement. For, there would be no début by Flora Sommerton that evening. She had plans that would prevent her ever again crossing the threshold of her parents' preposterously ornate house.

Perhaps, Flora mused, she would never have planned this drastic step if her mother—and, of course, her father, forever quaking in his wife's presence—had not demanded that she marry Hugh Partridge. Hugh was a dissolute, tittering snob and a weak fool, and she despised him.

Flora had asked her singing teacher, Miss Englehardt, what chance she had of earning a living with her voice.

Miss Englehardt had been kind but evasive. "My dear Flora, I can think of nothing more remote than that you should ever have to earn your own living. Your voice is light; it has a sweet tone. But your diction is extremely poor. You must spend a great deal of time studying before you try singing to an audience professionally."

Flora had smiled and left Miss Englehardt's studio. "Well," she had said to herself, "perhaps I can teach singing."

The afternoon was growing short. Flora hastened her step until she arrived at a shop at the foot of California Street. There she gave Billy, the delivery boy, a note she had written to her mother; he was to leave it at the Sommertons' when he made his deliveries to Nob Hill.

Billy delivered his note to the service door of the Sommerton house at six o'clock. Belowstairs there was such confusion that the envelope was mislaid. At seven o'clock, Mrs. Sommerton, in the hands of her French hairdresser, demanded to know where Miss Flora was.

No one knew. None of the servants had seen her since lunch. All afternoon, the house had been in a flurry of preparations for the ball.

"Yes, yes!" said Carrie Sommerton impatiently. "She was going for a walk but that was hours ago."

Aunt Helene was awakened in her room by the running up and down stairs. She opened her door and cried out that she would look a fright if she was not allowed some rest before the soirée.

Then, just as the head of the house of Sommerton was being relieved of his hat and stick in the marble entrance hall, one of the housemaids suddenly remembered the note. It was fetched to Mrs. Sommerton, she read it, and for an hour the quiet of the grave reigned on the second floor of the great house. Carrie Sommerton called her husband and her sister Helene to her boudoir. Though the night was uncomfortably warm, heavy curtains were drawn closely across the four windows looking out over the city. The door was locked, and the three laid plans of how this crisis was to be met.

For Carrie, humiliation was unthinkable. Never once did she show the faintest concern about what might happen to her sheltered eighteen-year-old daughter, unprotected in a half-barbarous city. Pride ruled Carrie, and only her pride was considered.

Her husband timidly suggested that they should call in the police, but Carrie scotched that at once. "Don't be a fool, Charlie. She must have taken money enough to support herself for a while. We'll go through with this ball. We'll say she is ill and had to be sent to the country, but that she insisted we go on with the arrangements as if she were here. Tomorrow we can start to trace her. And we will find her, never fear."

Aunt Helene sat as if she were in a trance, the letter held loosely in her hand. Carrie reached out and took it. For the fourth time, she read it aloud, grimly.

> *"Dear Mamma:*
> *I want to make this letter short. I am going away to make my own life. I have planned carefully. For a long time I had thought of it. Then you insisted I marry Hugh. I just could not face that. I have some money, and my jewelry. Also I have a trained singing voice . That may help me to earn a living. Do not try to find me. You, nor Pa, nor the police ever could. Don't think me heartless.*
>
> > *Flora"*

The grand ball at the Sommerton's, which was to have introduced their only daughter to society, took place as scheduled. On the dot of ten o'clock, Mr. and Mrs. Charles Benbow Sommerton and Miss Helene Marvin took their places, standing rigidly in a row on the landing of the staircase that wound its gleaming marble way, roped in smilax and calla lilies, to a series of reception rooms above.

The three welcomers on the stairs presented a study in contrasts. Carrie Sommerton was a monument of icy graciousness, Charles was sad-eyed, and Helene fluttered constantly on the edge of tears. Whenever a guest asked where Flora was, Carrie answered briefly, "She was taken suddenly ill. Nerves. I sent her to the country."

To this, Charles and Helene nodded agreement.

Not everybody believed it. As the Tobins, the Parrots, the Lloyd Tevises, the Haggins, the Phelans, the Leland Stanfords, the Coltons, the Fairs, and the Crockers—all nabobs—ascended the stairs, conjecture waxed high.

A woman with a high-pitched voice exclaimed, "I'd give a lot to know what really is up. Unless Flora had bubonic plague, Carrie would have bolstered her up somehow for tonight." "Charlie looks green around the gills," a man remarked. "Wonder where the girl got to?"

Nevertheless, the soirée, as Helene, the Francophile, called every evening party, was a resounding success. The orchestra was perfection. All the popular waltzes of the day were played. The brilliantly lighted reception rooms and *anti-covert* marble ballroom, with its gold-leaf cornice and column capitals, throbbed to gaiety. Through it all, Carrie was an indefatigable hostess.

At twelve o'clock, the Circassian walnut doors of the huge dining room were thrown open. A portly, smiling *gros bonnet*, recently arrived from Paris, presided at a buffet of formidable proportions.

Opulence was the keystone of parties on Nob Hill during the last decades of the nineteenth century. Almost incalculable fortunes had come from the famed Comstock Lode and other, now legendary mining projects. It was an era when a few canny promoters grasped and held tightly the horns of plenty. Riches flowed for a time, then, as suddenly as a veering wind, ceased. In this fantastic era of California history, one was either gold or silver or railroad rich.

No woman on Nob Hill had greater ambitions, or more money to gratify them, than Carrie Sommerton. As she stood in the doorway and watched the élite of San Francisco—even a few choice guests from that Baghdad of the East Coast, New York City—devour her pheasant in *foie gras,* sherried terrapin, truffled galantine of guinea hen, and magnums of Perrier Jouet, she could not forget that Flora, her quiet, submissive daughter, had spiked her most important plans. She had defeated Carrie's greatest maneuver to date—an alliance with a family of blue blood. Carrie could brazen out a ball on an excuse no one believed, but to face Mrs. Mortimer Partridge, who only tolerated her because no one better than Flora had turned up, was more than she could bear.

As a brassy sun rose to treat San Francisco to another muggy day, the last carriage drove from under the porte-cochere of the Sommerton house. The ball was over.

Uneasy days followed. Charles Sommerton called in the police and a search for Flora began. He offered a reward of two hundred and fifty thousand dollars. Cranks responded and leads were followed, with no result. Flora had disappeared leaving no trace.

Numerous things were missing from Flora's room. Carrie looked for, and did not find, the lovely gown Aunt Helene had brought Flora from Paris for her début. It was a dress out of a fairy tale—yards and yards of white tulle, a draped satin sash, and the whole powdered with infinitesimal crystal beads.

When Flora had tried the dress on for the first time, she was rapturous. "I look as if I had been caught in a gale of frost crystals. It is the most beautiful dress I ever saw," she said.

"Treacherous, that is what Flora is—treacherous," Carrie said, pacing her boudoir. "She pretended she was happy while she schemed to get away. Make her own life, indeed. As much chance as a white kitten chased by a pack of mongrel dogs."

The days lengthened into weeks, the weeks into months. From the day of her début, when she had entered the store on California Street and asked the delivery boy to take a note to her mother, neither friends nor family saw Flora again. She seemed to have walked into limbo. The dénouement occurred, eventually, in Butte, Montana.

Many clues were followed, to no avail, by the police and detectives in the employ of Charles Sommerton. About three years after Flora's disappearance, a lodging-house-keeper in Kansas City became suspicious of a young woman who had taken her big front parlor to give singing lessons. The girl gave the name of Brown and was pretty but meek, according to the landlady. The lodger had put out a sign announcing that singing and piano lessons could be had. Some pupils had appeared, but they soon dropped off. One girl told the landlady, "She's no good. She can't teach, and I can sing as good as she can, anyhow."

The lodger paid her rent promptly for three weeks. She had brought along little baggage, but she had one large paper-covered bundle she seemed to value.

One night, the landlady, passing the door of the front parlor heard her lodger coughing heavily. She knocked and opened the door, asking if there was anything she could do. The girl was bright-eyed from fever. Clutching the woman's arm, the girl said, "If anything should happen to me—if I'm sick, I mean—don't send me to a hospital. Send me to the Sisters of Mary Convent, on Clary Street."

A few days later, the girl was much better. Meanwhile, a neighbor, in talking to the landlady, mentioned that the police were still looking for the Sommerton girl from San Francisco. The landlady went to the local police station, and not long afterward, accompanied by a plainclothesman, she knocked at the door of the front parlor. The lodger had departed. A few of her belongings lay scattered about in confusion, but the big paper-wrapped bundle was gone.

The Sommerton house on Nob Hill burned down in the San Francisco fire. Charles died, and Carrie, accompanied by Helene, set up household in a showy, turreted house near Cypress Point, a few miles from San Francisco. By that time, Carrie had almost forgotten she had ever had a daughter. With the death of Charles, Carrie called off the hunt.

Then, one day, the San Francisco police brought a letter to Mrs. Sommerton. It was from the prima donna of a third-rate traveling company presenting "The Prince of Pilsen" in Los Angeles. The woman, who signed herself Adele La Blanche, felt sure she could supply information about Flora. The big reward still shone like a beacon; through the years it had lain dormant in a San Francisco bank.

Adele La Blanche's story was this. A few months back, while the company was giving performances in Chicago, she had slipped and sprained her ankle on an icy pavement. When it was learned that she could not go on for a few performances, her understudy, a Miss Jarvis, took over. But the understudy was a far more slender woman than La Blanche; the costumes for the prima-donna role did not fit. Then a dresser to the women of the ensemble—a quiet, faded middle-aged woman—came forward and said she had a dress that would probably do.

Within an hour, the dresser returned from her lodgings with a huge brown-paper bundle. Out of it she took an entrancing gown, no longer in style but of lovely design. It was made of pure-white tulle, sprinkled, like the heavens on a starry night, with crystal beads. The woman pressed the gown, and Miss Jarvis wore it with great success. When La Blanche returned to the show, she tried to buy the dress to have it altered for her own use. Her conversation with the dresser had caused her to write the letter.

After a long silence, the woman had said, "No, I cannot sell it. You see it is my only link with the past. It is Nob Hill and what I might have been." A startled look had come into her eyes, and she had taken her dress and fled, again leaving no trace.

About 1916, Carrie Sommerton died, blind, in seclusion. Her last years were lonely and bitter ones. Helene had, oddly, married a Mormon and disappeared inside a mammoth house in Salt Lake City. The gimcrack house Carrie had built at Cypress Point after the great fire was sold for a golf club. Later, it was torn down to enlarge the course.

Intermittently, letters were received by San Francisco authorities giving clues of the whereabouts of Flora Sommerton. Then, in 1926, a paragraph appeared in a Butte, Montana, newspaper, reading, "A woman working as a housekeeper in a downtown hotel was found dead in her bed this morning under curious circumstances. No hint of foul play is entertained. The coroner's verdict is death from heart disease. The woman, who called herself Mrs. Butler, was about fifty-seven years old. She had been employed at Butte Central Hotel, a commercial hostelry, for ten years. The police are not satisfied that her name was Butler. In a small valise was found a sheaf of newspaper clippings from San Francisco, and others from widely scattered newspapers. Most of them dated from 1876 to 1891. These clippings refer in detail to the worldwide search for Flora Sommerton, the eighteen-year-old daughter of Charles Sommerton, multimillionaire of Nob Hill, San Francisco. The discovery of the deceased's body by a housemaid was something of a sensation. The figure, lying on the narrow bed in a cheerless hotel room, was dressed in a white ball gown of the eighteen-eighties. Entirely covered in crystal beads, the dress bore the label of a Paris dressmaker. San Francisco police have been notified."

The ghost of Flora Sommerton has come back to Nob Hill—not, by a long way, the Nob Hill she knew on that far-off afternoon when she sauntered along California Street. Scarcely a house now remains where friends of her girlhood lived. At night, as she walks past the Pacific Union Club, she doubtless recalls it as the mansion of James Flood, one of the first bonanza kings whose flamboyant way of living dazzled the nation.

After Flora died, clothed in crystal in a mean hotel in Butte, her body was brought back to San Francisco and buried in the family plot. The reward, of-fered years before by her father, was taken from the bank and given to charity.

Now people report seeing a girl, in a shimmering white dress, strolling in streets and gardens in the Nob Hill section of the city. She seems to be return-ing from a late party. The figure smiles at passersby and moves in a leisurely manner. As in her life, Flora is still walking alone.

MAD ANTHONY

FOUR ANECDOTES ABOUT MAJOR GENERAL ANTHONY WAYNE

ONE OF THE most vivid characters in American military history is Major General Anthony Wayne, a man of exceeding courage and daring. Many were the rash but successful escapades credited to this powerfully built son of a Yorkshire yeoman.

Everything about the man—his stature, his Gargantuan appetite—befitted heroic scale. When he camped at Storm King, and, later, at Stony Point, after the rout and capture of the British garrison, his resonant far-reaching laughter reverberated through the valley. Indeed, his guffaws were said by Hudson River Valley dwellers to rival the sound of midnight revels by "Dutch bowlers" in the glens.

History records Anthony Wayne's proverbial bravery and his notable performance as military tactician. An accomplished horseman, he bred a fine type of hunter—a large-boned animal suitable for riders of his extraordinary build—from Vermont and the Genesee Valley when he was stationed at Fort Ticonderoga.

Two other facets to this man's nature command attention—his success with, and overweening predilection for, the ladies, and his ability as a ghost to appear in so many different roles in so many different places that he must surely be the busiest and most traveled ghost on record. Of the many stories told about him, I have chosen four.

The Smile That Broke
The Widow's Heart

FORT TICONDEROGA, 1771

THE FIRST STORY begins when General Anthony Wayne was given command of Fort Ticonderoga, dominating the icy blue waters of Lake Champlain near Crown Point, a post much to his liking. Many of his friends among the officers of the Continental Army were stationed there. The cavalry was hand-picked; the living quarters and parade ground proved to be excellent. Wayne, accustomed to tough campaigning and dangerous scouting missions, expanded in the midst of comfort and the joviality of good companionship.

One other item he chalked up as highly complimentary to the countryside. There were plenty of handsome women—married or single, it was all one to the doughty General—living in fine houses scattered about the countryside, from Pells to Montpelier, in Vermont, and from Glen Falls to Utica, in New York. The land in this part of the country was fertile; Demeter was generous with her fruits. Yes, life promised to be pleasant and interesting for Anthony Wayne.

As at any fort, Ticonderoga had its women camp followers. Some of the cavalrymen had brought their wives with them. Washerwomen, seamstresses, and girls whose reason for being there needed no inquiry lived in a number of small brick and stone cottages, usually of one or two rooms, that clung to a wall of the fort.

During its years of usefulness, Fort Ticonderoga changed hands frequently.

84

Sometimes the French from Canada stamped the snow in the rectangular drill yard. Twice the British kept the American Army at bay by continuous fire from the fort batteries. Meanwhile, the living quarters, for officers and enlisted men alike, changed in character with the habits of the men who occupied them.

When Anthony Wayne arrived as commandant, he found the luxuriously appointed quarters of Lord Jeffrey Amherst, but lately quitted by Ethan Allen. To celebrate his appointment, the General gave a dinner party, and there two feminine faces caught his eye. One was the ravishingly pretty dimpled face of the daughter of Prescott Haynes, a wealthy landowner from Montpelier way; the other was the healthily flushed impudent face and the buxom posterior of Nancy Coates, who was helping serve at the General's table.

Mistress Coates professed to be a widow, although no one could ever remember having seen a husband in her train of admirers. That Nancy had plenty of suitors was evident from the glow of the tallow dip that was seen to flicker long past the ten-o'clock "all in quarters" bugle, which sounded nightly. Often a hasty good night was heard at her door well after midnight. But Nancy was a good-natured woman, always willing to lend a hand to help, and her neighbors pretended to believe she was a respectable widow. No woman of Nancy's station at the garrison dressed as smartly as she. All sorts of little fribbles and bows adorned her chintz bodices on a Sunday morning, when she, with the other inhabitants of Fort Ticonderoga, took the air on the parade ground or walked abroad on the paths, outside the fort, along the lake shore. Here, where the trees grew close together, many an Indian savage had ambushed French, British, or American soldiers.

Soon after the dinner party, General Wayne was standing, one evening, at the window of his quarters, idly surveying the landscape. His thoughts were mixed. He had been invited to the Haynes mansion in Montpelier for the night, and, though he wanted to go, it was impossible. Important dispatches from General Washington were due to arrive the next morning, and he had to remain at the fort to receive them in person. Just then, a figure in a print gown and a hooded mantle of dark red passed slowly under his window. By jackery! It was that tempting piece who had handed round the pudding at his dinner party. He'd practically had to sit on his hands not to pinch her bottom. Mighty tempting. Well, she seemed to be in no hurry. What was to hinder him taking a breath of air along the lake?

So started a flirtation between Anthony Wayne and Nancy Coates that was to lead to tragic consequences, though nothing seemed less likely during their first cordial encounter by the lake. Other agreeable evenings followed for the handsome, compelling suitor and the blushing, eager-to-please widow. Each time, the fulfillment of ardent desires left the General in good humor—nothing more. But to Nancy Coates the fabric of her love grew in leaps and bounds. However trifling she had been in the past, this was the love of her life, and she knew it.

One night, as Nancy lay in Wayne's arms, the floodgates burst. She told him of her love. "What shall we do?" she asked anxiously. "Will you marry me? I could live away from the fort somewhere."

To all her suggestions, Anthony remained cool. In fact, he was annoyed. Why couldn't women take a light view of these affairs? Even the thought of marriage was ridiculous. The General rallied his forces, which were formidable; he left the widow mollified, if exhausted.

Meanwhile, the British were becoming increasingly bold. General Wayne received a message from his Commander-in-Chief saying that skirmishes in outlying districts of New York State and Vermont had aroused and frightened the people. Prescott Haynes and some other influential men asked for protection for their womenfolk within the walls of Fort Ticonderoga. Would General Wayne send a detachment of cavalry to bring in the women named on the accompanying list?

As Wayne ran his eye down the column, he smiled. He would comply with General Washington's request in person. He himself would escort Miss Penelope Haynes to the fort. Her mother he would put in an Army wagon with some other women. As for Miss Penelope, she would ride pillion with him on Nab.

Anthony Wayne did not see Nancy Coates again before he set out for Montpelier. When she asked about his absence, some of the women of the alley, as the space where the cottages hugged the fort walls was called, thought to play a joke on her. "Why, dearie me," one said. "Didn't the General tell you? He's ridden off, gay as you please, to bring back his bride from Montpelier." The women standing nearby cackled with laughter.

But to Nancy, terrified by Wayne's silence since their last meeting, this message was far from funny. Could it be true? She sought out one of the officers to whom she had given her favors before Wayne had arrived. Was it true what she had been told by those bitches? Lieutenant Carstairs shrugged. Here was a way to pay back the flighty Nancy for shunting him off the minute that ox Wayne hove into sight.

"Certainly it's true. Why not? It's the Haynes girl. He's bringing her mother along, and a lot of friends to make it a gay wedding. I expect you'll be there as maid of honor." He went off laughing.

Nancy believed these tales. The thought that he was really bringing back a bride sent her distractedly wandering about the lake-shore paths.

A few days later, at dusk, everyone at the fort was alerted by the sound of a bugle call coming from the road outside the gates. Immediately, a sentry fired a welcoming shot and a bugler leaped onto the lookout walk to wind an answering call. Word spread rapidly that General Wayne and his escort were approaching.

The first notes of the bugle startled Nancy Coates, who, that evening, after walking aimlessly about, had thrown herself down on the ground under a pine tree. Running like one pursued, she gained the fort gate just as the platoon of cavalry, followed by a wagon train, rode under the arch.

Her hand flew to her mouth when she saw the General. As always, Anthony rode Nab. He led the wagon train wherein groups of women waved to friends and laughed and chattered like starlings. As Nab passed Nancy, she looked into the face of Anthony Wayne. He was smiling over his shoulder at a young girl who sat pillion behind him. The hood of her peach-colored cloak had slipped back, and her auburn hair floated about her face in lovely disarray. Nancy put out her hand and touched the boot of the man, who still smiled at his companion. But Wayne appeared quite unconscious of the woman, and she stumbled, sobbing, back among the crowd cheering at the gates.

Nancy turned away and raced down the path to the lake. It was true; all that the laughing gossipers had said was true. The moon came up and moved stealthily across an indigo sky. Hours later, dawn streaked the horizon with faint rose. The woman sitting by the lake, her head upon her knees, got slowly to her feet. For a while, she stood, as if undecided, looking up at the walls of the fort. All was quiet there. Boards creaked under a sentry's tread. Nothing more. With a sigh of utter wretchedness, the woman walked out into the waters of the lake.

Later in the day, two soldiers, bound for a bit of fishing, discovered the body of Nancy Coates drifting in the reeds a mile or so from the fort.

Nancy's death was sadly ironic. Anthony Wayne had neither intention, nor inclination to marry Penelope Haynes, however pretty and gay, or any other woman. He was not a marrying man. He had simply been engrossed in the sprightly conversation of the girl he had been asked to conduct to the fort, and had never felt the touch of the woman's hand on his boot.

Fort Ticonderoga is now a national monument. One may wander about the fortification at will. The spacious quarters once occupied by General Wayne are furnished as they might have been when he gave his first dinner party.

It is told that often at nightfall a distracted woman hovers about the gate to the fort. She has also been observed, in happier mood, walking through the guardroom of the garrison and loitering up and down the alley, a stretch of cobbles where cottages once stood.

Summer campers have seen a weeping woman running along the lake paths. One man told of taking a rowboat out onto the lake on an insufferably hot night. He was just about to dive over for a swim, when he heard loud sobbing coming from a reedy stretch along the shore. Thinking someone needed help, the man rowed to the spot, where he saw the body of a woman, floating face upward, among the reeds. He moved toward it, but the body, just out of reach, drifted away into the darkness, and the sobbing faded into silence.

The ghost of General Wayne is said to appear in the dining room of the commandant's quarters at the fort. A man of huge frame, wearing the uniform and gold lace of a general of the Continental Army, sits at a table, poring over maps far into the night. At dawn, he rises, stretches himself, and belches loudly.

At other times, this figure is seen reclining comfortably in a wing chair before the fireplace, smoking a churchwarden pipe and drinking from a pewter mug. To observers, it is not difficult to identify this ghost, for he is a counterpart of the portrait of General Anthony Wayne that hangs on a wall of this room.

The Twin Eagles

VERMONT-CANADIAN BORDER, 1776

NOW LET us go back a year, back to the time when Anthony Wayne was leading a scouting party in the wilds of Canada. It appears that two half-breed guides, who lived as trappers in the forests and along the lakes and rivers of Laurentian Canada, offered to take the Major and a friend to a place where some bald eagles had built their aerie. The guides said there were four or five eaglets in the nest. If caught early and trained, this bird made as fine a hunting companion as one would wish.

On a cold, clear morning, the party set out. For a few miles, the way lay over water. The rapids of a river were negotiated, and the men set off across scrubland, first hiding their canoe in a thicket. At noon, they came to a high, jagged rock with a wide cleft at the peak. Sticking out from this cleft, at right angles, were what looked like limbs of a tree laid helter-skelter. This was the eagle nest. One lone bird circled around the nest, high up, as if on guard while others quested for food. Keeping hidden in underbrush, the men waited until the eagle had settled on a ledge of rock near the nest. Then one of the guides, who was an accomplished bowman, crept to within range. With a single arrow, he brought the eagle tumbling down the rocks, shot through the throat.

Now, in haste, before the other eagle, or eagles, returned from foraging, the men scaled the rock. They found only two eaglets in the nest, twin bald heads, far more grown than anyone had expected. A fight to remove the birds followed, and one of them raked Anthony Wayne across the cheek and the bridge of his nose. He carried the scar of this wound the rest of his life, and, according to the ladies, it added a definitely romantic look to his face.

89

Finally, the fighting eaglets bagged, the hunting party returned to the canoe and so proceeded back to camp.

From then on, until, at a good age, the eagles died, Anthony Wayne kept them in light reed cages in his baggage train. He himself attended to rearing them and teaching them the art of falconry. Many were the fine days of casting for prey that Wayne and his twin baldheads enjoyed. When a man once asked him what he called them, he said, "Collectively, they are North West Passage. This one," pointing to the bird that had raked his face, "is North. This one," pointing to the less fractious of the twins, "is West. Their family name is Passage. I call them so because of the fight we had securing them."

Life with North and West was not all pleasure, according to chroniclers. When the eagles were not hooded, they caused plenty of ruckus. Once, when a hunting party was leaving the fort, a boy flung a stone, hitting Wayne's horse on the flank. The horse threw his head back, striking one of the eagles, who flew into a rage and ripped the horse with his lethal beak, severing a blood vessel.

Wayne had to be forever on the alert lest the birds, which he often carried on a specially mounted staghorn strapped to the pommel of his saddle, fly at him. What amused him most was to cast both birds at a prey, watch them rise together, swoop at the same time, and then have a short fight in midair to settle which one would bring back the kill.

After Anthony Wayne died, he was reported to haunt the log fort at Lake Memphremagog, which had become a fur traders' post. In the moonlight, his giant figure, dressed in the fringed leathers of an Indian scout, walked along the shore of the lake, arms outstretched. Sitting on each wrist, surveying the midnight world with arrogant disdain, were twin baldheaded eagles. What frightened the wits out of Canuck trappers and their women was the fact that whenever Mad Anthony wished to cross the lake, he did so unhesitatingly, at any point, and his moccasined feet scarcely touched the water.

Fire and Brimstone at Stony Point

HUDSON RIVER VALLEY, NEW YORK STATE, 1779

STORIES of the daring adventures of Mad Anthony Wayne and his powerful raw-boned bay stallion, Nab, may be somewhat embellished. Indeed, most ghost stories worth listening to are highly pointed up. These yarns are told and retold with zest over mugs of applejack in the river taverns. There are raftered farmhouses in the meadowland under the beetling heights of Storm King Mountain and the rise behind Stony Point, and many a family in these farmhouses has gathered round the fire to bequeath the stories to their children. The tales are still told today.

Mad Anthony Wayne's night ride on Nab, to warn the American troops at Storm King Pass of the impending attack on the British garrison, remains one of the most heroic exploits of the entire War of Independence. This is how it happened:

Everyone in the vicinity of the American Army Headquarters at Hudson Point knew that, left to his own devices, Wayne would order Nab saddled for a ride in the lonely hills. The two heartily enjoyed racing off along the rocky mountain roads, night or day—roads that a careful rider would take at a slow pace even in broad daylight. More timid men shook their heads, murmuring that Nab was the embodiment of Old Nick himself.

Then, one night in the year 1779, General Washington commissioned Anthony Wayne to ride, alone, practically into the bivouac of the enemy. It was necessary to warn the American troops at Storm King Pass that a surprise attack, with bayonets, was to take place at midnight. No one knew the road as well as

91

Anthony Wayne and Nab. In the teeth of a gale of tempest volume, Wayne rode to warn the troops, returning just in time to take command of the bayonet attack on Stony Point and win the heights. It was this achievement, more than any other, that gained for General Wayne the sobriquet Mad Anthony. General Washington brevetted him Major General.

A strange story sprang up along the Hudson Valley after this mad ride. It was remarked that as Wayne and Nab tore along Storm King Pass, the horse not only struck the sparks natural to horseshoes striking on flint but also trailed blue and orange sparks from his hide wherever a branch touched him. Pure brimstone, that horse!

Today many riverside dwellers declare that on stormy nights a horseman gallops along a narrow pass among the rocks of Storm King Mountain. The rider, a dark figure in cocked hat and Army cloak, huddles over the withers of his horse, a spectacular beast.

"There goes Mad Anthony Wayne and Nab," a watcher will say. "Means there's a big storm brewing. Probably one of Satan's own, too. Guess I'll bar my shutters tonight." A group of cronies will stand in a tavern doorway gazing up the mountain at the crouched rider on his flying mount. The horse is a shimmering streak of articulated brimstone, followed by a cometlike tail of phosphorus sparks.

In the days, not so long past, when that pleasant American institution, the Albany night boat, plied the mountain-reflected waters of the Hudson River, it was customary for amorous couples to sit on deck far into the night. Many trippers recounted having seen, when passing Storm King Mountain or Stony Point, a streak of light spitting orange sparks and traveling at tremendous speed in and out of the rock-tunneled mountain roads.

Sometimes the speeding aura of light was so bright that one could make out the silhouette of a cloaked figure bending over the neck of a horse. On the two sped, Mad Anthony Wayne and his beloved Nab, reliving the exhilarating night rides through the mountains that both had once so heartily enjoyed.

"The House of My Heart's Desire"

NOLAND HOUSE, LOUDOUN COUNTY, VIRGINIA, 1750

I N 1777, General Anthony Wayne led his army out of Fort Ticonderoga, surrendering it to General Burgoyne. "The bitterest pill I ever had to swallow," the General said to Lieutenant Shaw, his aide-de-camp. He swung around in the saddle to take one last look at Old Carillon—a name that had stuck to the fortification since it was erected, in 1775, by the French.

As the long line of soldiers marched, two abreast, along the narrow mountain road, Wayne said to Shaw, "We are to join General Lafayette at Rapidan, and on the way, I will be able to see the house of my heart's desire." Shaw smiled. Wayne said, "Yes,—don't laugh—I have my heart set on a house I once saw in Loudoun County. Philip Noland was building it. It wasn't finished, but there was a salubrious air about it. That's the house I would like to own someday, a place to cross my swords over the chimney place, take off my boots, stretch my legs to the blaze, and—let me see—take a pretty woman on my knee."

Two hundred years ago, Anthony Wayne voiced his desire for a Georgian brick house that he had seen only half finished. He would probably be surprised to see Noland House today, for it is still not finished.

Long before the white man came, a trail was blazed from the Potomac to Kentucky and the twin Carolinas. Rogues' Road, the trail was called, for, very like Natchez Trace, in Mississippi, a shifty, murderous kind of customer roamed the Indian paths. These migrants, who were adept at all thieveries, were finally driven out about 1780. A small village sprang up, and close to this a tract of "salubrious acres" was acquired by a rich Colonial planter named Philip Noland. ("Salubrious" was a favorite adjective for the heavily foliaged properties of Virginia. Lady Fairfax, widow of the Colonial Governor, named her house Salubria.)

On a slight rise embowered in oak shade, Philip Noland started building his house. Important in scale and size, with four stories of red brick and two massive chimneys crowning the gables, the house embraced many elegant features. The spacious library had tall arched bookcases. There was even a small ballroom, thirty-odd feet by seventeen. The entrance hall, lighted by a glass fan over the door, contained a staircase as graceful as any in Virginia.

On one of Anthony Wayne's many scouting expeditions, he had met Noland, who, like all builders, eagerly exhibited his rising house. Noland House apparently struck a deep chord in the mind of Wayne. Hitherto he had lived in camps, tepees, or the chancy, makeshift quarters of barracks. The longing for a home, where he could settle down, ranked high in his desires.

All manner of strange occurrences hindered the finishing of Noland House. Some Virginians say Philip Noland lost a great deal of money when he signed a promissory note for a neighbor, who later died bankrupt. Then his wife, who was Elizabeth Aubrey, inherited a fortune, but it dwindled away in litigation.

Near Noland House was a camp of Hessian prisoners captured at Saratoga. A story is told that some of these Hessians were conscripted to work on the house, and during a sudden cold spell a log fire, lighted in the cellar to keep them warm, set the house afire. Later, three of the Hessians escaped from the prison camp, taking refuge in the vacant Noland House. The men were tracked there, and in trying to elude their pursuers two were shot and killed. The ghosts of these men prowl through the cellar regions at night, pounding and scratching on the walls to get out.

In 1778, Anthony Wayne camped for a time near Harper's Ferry, prior to joining Lafayette at the Rapidan River. He probably visited the house of his friend Noland many times. One wonders if he puzzled, as we admirers of the house do today, over the slowness of construction. Even now, bare whitewashed stone walls await plaster or wood paneling. No steps lead to the front door. Dadoes and cornices are lacking in some of the rooms. Was it ever furnished at all?

Considering that Wayne is so wandering a ghost, I fancy he often visits the Noland place, which, in spite of neglect and mutilation by tenant farmers, is still an extremely handsome building. Pinching his lower lip, pushing his cocked hat over his eyes, I venture he walks through the mildewed rooms, asking of the bare walls, "Why the devil doesn't Philip get on with this house?"

Red Barn on the Hill
Gray Barn in the Valley

CHERRY VALLEY, NEW YORK STATE, 1890

THIS IS the story of Samantha Randall, who lived in a farmhouse in Cherry Valley, a green, brook-fed area near Cooperstown. Samantha Randall was a woman of staunch pioneer caliber, a good woman. But the Furies rode her hard.

Both Samantha and Justin, her husband, were born in the valley. Their families had come from Kentucky, driving wagon track, before the Revolution. Indeed, Justin's grandfather had been scalped by an Oneida brave when Indians were still rampageous in the lake region.

As a marriage dowry, Oriskiny Brockett, Samantha's father, the most prosperous farmer in the region, had given her a ninety-acre farm. The day the bride and groom drove over to set up housekeeping, Samantha exclaimed in delight, "What a tidy little house! And look at that big silver-colored barn, Justin!"

The groom, a morose man, was not so easily pleased, for secretly he felt his father-in-law could have been more generous to his only daughter. He grunted, and said, "Barn's big as a meetin' house. Too many trees to uproot to plant crops. House ain't big enough fer raisin' a family."

But the two did raise a family. Three children grew up in this green valley, building beaver dams in the brook, playing in the big haymows of the silver barn.

Seth, the first-born, was a tall, ungainly lad with a nature sweet as spring

95

water. Mary, who followed, seemed more like her father, sullen-natured and grasping. Then came Orrin, the turkey cock, always strutting, deceitful, proud as Lucifer. From early childhood, he admired everything big-scaled, gaudy, pretentious. Into the bargain, he was cruel to the farm animals.

One day, when Orrin was six years old, he was playing in the brook with a birch-bark canoe he had made. Samantha stood on her back porch, as she often did, looking at the barn, for it was, indeed, a beautiful object. Never had paint touched the long hand-adzed planks, and after years of exposure they buckled and waved, casting the whole off center. Time had encrusted the boards with a rime of moss and bronze-gray lichen. At high noon, it took on a green-gold shimmer; in moon and star shine, it gleamed stark silver, like some ancient Attic temple to Diana.

As she stood daydreaming, Samantha was suddenly yanked back to reality by a loud commotion at the duckpond. A mother duck with a brood of goslings clamored wildly in protest. Then Orrin came to the porch, poised triumphantly, and hurled a gosling whose neck he had wrung almost at his mother's feet. "It pecked me when I tried to pick it up." The boy raised his chin. "I showed it. I'll always show 'em."

For days, Samantha went about her chores silently. She scarcely spoke, even to her favorite, Seth. At first, she would not admit to herself the fact that tormented her. She would stop in the midst of a task and stand staring into space. Finally, the realization came to her—she hated Orrin, and had for a long while, though he was only a child. The jut of his jaw told her he would grow worse. He would grow up a cruel, hard man.

Samantha was a quiet, withdrawn woman, and time did not ease her thoughts. At the village stores, where the wives of farmers met for gossip as well as purchase, Samantha Randall was often discussed.

"I never see such a change in a body, these last few months," remarked Cally Dunlop, from Beeksford Bridge.

"I know what you mean," old Miss Purdy answered. "She don't come to the sewing bees no more. Nor the cake sales. If I meet her, she nods kinda absent-minded like. Well, livin' with that piece of impudence Mary Randall and her pa would throw me off my feed."

The women returned to shopping, nodding their heads in agreement.

The years passed more or less quietly at the Randall farm. Seth was not much of a scholar, preferring the woods and meadows to any books. All animal life loved him, had no fear of his presence. He left school at sixteen and, with his mother's help, ran the farm.

Mary was her father's girl, and to him she talked constantly of her plans to leave the farm for a job in Albany or Troy. In the evenings, she would go out to the workshop Justin had fitted up for himself in a corner of the barn. Here he puttered endlessly at not much of anything; he was the least handy man at farming, or with tools, anyone had ever seen.

Finally, when Mary was eighteen, she wheedled her father into giving her a hundred dollars to start her on a career in the city. She never asked her mother's permission.

At breakfast on the day she was to leave, Samantha said to her, "I see you're all dressed for travelin'. You won't stay long, wherever it is you're goin'. Ye ain't got it in you. Too much like your shiftless pa." But she gave her daughter a purse of money, and a basket of food to eat on the train. "Goodbye, Mary," her mother said. "You can always come back when you want to."

Mary Randall never came back. After working as a waitress in a hotel in Troy, she married a vaudeville actor who was as rascally as they come. Trailing about the country and living in cheap lodgings sapped Mary's health. For a while, she wrote to Justin. Then he died, and the letters stopped. Nothing was ever heard of Mary again.

Orrin grown to a big, black-haired man, raised pure hell in the villages of Cherry Valley, drinking, brawling, and messing with women of bad stamp. But he managed to keep himself in funds by taking all manner of jobs, usually of short duration. Sometimes, after an amatory bout when he had been rooked for a fair sum of money, he would come back to the farm. This tormented Seth and infuriated Samantha. He would laze around or putter in the workshop. After a time, he would depart, as suddenly as he came, for another cast at fortune.

Then, one summer, Seth was badly hurt when out cutting wood. The rotted branch of a huge lightning-blasted maple tree fell from the parent trunk, crushing his skull and shoulders. Samantha nursed her boy night and day. Dr. Derby, the family physician, called in a bone specialist from Albany, but on the evening of the tenth day after the accident Seth Randall died in his mother's arms. That night Samantha stood for hours on the back porch, like one struck dumb, staring at the barn. The moonlight slid luminous fingers over the lopsided walls.

Dawn broke, and only then did the grieving woman move or speak. "They're all took from me but Orrin, my ungodly son. Why, oh why, God, was it Seth you took?" She broke into uncontrollable weeping.

After Seth died, Orrin arrived at his mother's farm one day with an announcement that she listened to standing stonily in the wide doorway of the barn. "I've got two thousand dollars. I'm going to buy the Huron farm. Up there." He flung out his arm in one of his elaborate gestures.

Samantha spoke from between tight lips. "You don't have to show me where the Huron place is. I've known Mat Huron all my life. Where'd ye get that money?"

Orrin smiled unpleasantly. "Don't matter none. I got it. I'm goin' up tonight to sign the papers."

No one ever found out, though many speculated, where the two thousand dollars came from. Some said Orrin bamboozled it out of an infatuated woman, years older than himself. It was well known that Mrs. Benson, a widow who owned the tavern in Cooperstown, had chased him for years.

He bought the farm and settled down to make it pay. Orrin, when he had a purpose, could work hard. The Huron farm was only fifty acres when he bought it. The farm buildings were in good repair. He hired one strong young farmhand. In three years, Orrin bought fifty acres of adjoining land with a fine stand of sugar maples covering half the acreage.

In all that time, he came down only once to the small white house in the valley. He wanted to buy the buzz saw that Seth had put in the sawmill beside the brook. Orrin, dressed in his Sunday best, stood in the doorway of the kitchen, where Samantha was taking her midday meal.

"You don't need to come in," she said. "What do you want?"

When her son told her she refused point-blank. "Go buy a buzz saw at Drayton's store. If you ever want to talk to me again, stop beatin' your horses. I saw you plowin' on the ridge. You punish those horses somethin' cruel. You're a godless brute. You're no son of mine. Now, get out!"

Samantha lived quietly through the years. She kept one cow, some poultry, and a few pigs. Each year, she had a man come for a day's pig-killing. She had a smokehouse for curing her hams and bacon. A small truck garden supplied her with fresh vegetables. She had no effect on the social life of the community, for she seldom left her farm.

People passing along the back road that skirted the lilac bushes fringing her yard often saw her, in a faded-blue print dress and a sunbonnet, out tending to her chores. In one hand she carried a forked stick to shoo hens and ducks and to ward off snakes. She was always prowling about her tree-shaded acres, often stopping to look up at the rapidly changing skyline of what used to be known as the Huron place. Now, since Orrin had built a second dairy barn, it was called Maple Ridge. Old Miss Purdy told Samantha that Orrin had put up fine stone gateposts and a fancy hanging sign, reading, "Maple Ridge Farm." Well, I'll never see it, Samantha thought.

Twelve years from the time Orrin Randall bought the fifty-acre farm, he increased it to nine hundred acres. He built twin silos, tall as church steeples and immense in circumference. These he painted vibrant red. About this time, the farmers of the valley began referring to the place as "Orrin Randall's village."

At night, Samantha would stand in the lee of her barn and shake her fist at the hilltop buildings, shining in the light cast by passing motorcars. "Proud as Lucifer," she would mutter. "Cruel as Pontius Pilate—smitten with greed. He's everything I hate. Never was no son of mine, rightly. Damnation'll find him out!"

In all fairness to Orrin, it must be said that about the time he put up the twin silos, which soon became landmarks dominating the countryside, he tried to induce his mother to come to the hilltop farmhouse to live. Dr. Derby had told him that she had grown frail and that her life of solitude was not good. Stoutly the indomitable woman refused all her son's offers.

"He's godless," she told Dr. Derby. "I'm a righteous woman. I'd be tainted with his badness if I lived under his roof."

By now, Orrin was becoming a power in Cherry Valley. One morning, he set out for a visit to the Pedigreed Cattle Show in Buffalo. Two months later he returned with a wife.

The woman he married, Marsha Ogden, matched Orrin in pride and arrogance. She was the daughter of Sheffield Ogden, a Lake Erie shipping magnate and leader of the "Lake aristocracy" of Buffalo. Marsha took one look at the big plain white farmhouse, built by Jacob Huron in 1800, and said, "Orrin, we simply cannot live here. How could I ask my friends from Buffalo to visit us! Oh, no. Let the superintendent live here."

Somewhat overawed by his elegant wife, Orrin immediately set about planning the construction of another house.

Soon a proud building was rising on the highest knoll of the farm, with massive chimneys, filigree-trimmed cupolas, and wide pillared verandahs that gave a magnificent view of the undulating valley. Marsha Randall was satisfied, and for a long time Orrin was virtually bankrupt. But he rallied, for his fortunes at that time seemed to be ringed by a charmed circle.

One day, suitably turned out, the lady from the hilltop took a long walk. Feeling adventurous, Marsha followed the little brook meandering so pleasantly along the floor of the valley at the foot of Maple Ridge. She lifted her mauve broadcloth skirt and crouched down to pick some trailing arbutus. Suddenly conscious of movement on the path, Marsha looked up. Standing not far away was a thin old woman in a faded dress and a sunbonnet. The next moment, without a glance at Marsha, the woman continued along the path, prodding a goose with a brood of noisy goslings.

Later, at dinner in her red-and-gold papered dining room, Marsha described her outing, and said "Orrin, who is that awful old woman who lives down in the valley? She looks like a scarecrow. I saw her today tending geese near that ramshackle barn."

There was a long silence. Orrin fingered his napkin nervously, wiped his mustache, and pushed his chair from the table. Rising, he started to leave the room. Then he paused behind his chair. In a cold voice, he said, "The woman is my mother. I lied to you. I said she lived in Cooperstown. Oh, well, you were bound to see her sometime." He left the room. Marsha never walked in the shady green valley again.

A son, Timothy, was born to Marsha and Orrin. He died in his sixth year. Meanwhile, in all things monetary Orrin prospered mightily.

The day of Timothy's funeral, Dr. Derby told Orrin his mother was gravely ill, probably on her deathbed. "Go to her, Orrin," the Doctor said. "Forget everything that has happened between you. She has asked for you."

Orrin shook his head. He must, he said, leave directly after the funeral to attend a meeting of bank directors in Cooperstown. On his return, in a day or so, he would go to the little house in the valley. Dr. Derby, who had brought Orrin into the world, tried to keep his voice civil. "It is serious, you know," he said. "Otherwise I would not have asked you to go."

Orrin pulled at his under lip. "Well," he said, "she's lived eighty-odd years. I doubt if she'll die tonight. I'll go on my return."

When Dr. Derby visited Samantha after the funeral of her grandson—a child she had seen from afar but never spoken to in his life—she demanded to know what Orrin had said.

The Doctor repeated the conversation.

Samantha sat up angrily. "I knew it. Pride and greed rule that man. Maybe it's some my fault. I've always held away from him since that day, years ago, when I saw how cruel he is. I can't stand cruelty. I always thought the Lord would punish him. Well, he hain't. Not yet. Orrin's prospered." The woman plucked at the sheet hem. "I'll see he's punished. He shan't escape." She sank back on the pillows and closed her eyes.

Dr. Derby had brought a woman from a neighboring farm to sit with his patient through the night. She built a hot fire in the potbellied stove, made tea, and settled down for her vigil. The heat and tiredness from a long day's work set her nodding. Soon she was deep in sleep, snoring lustily.

Outside it was a cold, windy night, brightly starry but without a moon. Slowly, about midnight, Samantha rose on one elbow. Listening, she satisfied herself the woman was fast asleep. She put one foot out of bed. Then the other. Under her breath she murmured, "I can stand. I'm stronger than I thought." Going to a clothes rack, she slipped on a wrapper. Then she took a long thick cape from behind the kitchen door and slipped silently onto the back porch. Steadying herself, Samantha drew the cape around her and walked to the barn. From a place where she had hidden it weeks before she took a meal sack containing a can of kerosene and a box of matches. Then she picked up her old forked stick and set off up the hill.

As she climbed slowly along the weed-tangled path, Samantha talked to herself. "I'll punish him. The Lord's too slow. My son must be punished. Little Timothy's taken. That's the first. Now I'll put fire to his greed."

Mumbling incoherently, the possessed woman climbed to the top of the ridge. Although neither Orrin nor his hired help knew about it, Samantha had often visited the red barns that dominated the ridge. In her long night watches, she had explored each building. She knew that livestock was kept in only one of them, the last in line away from the house. The wind blew in that direction tonight. Carefully she opened the doors of the cow barn. She went from yoke frame to yoke frame, liberating each cow so that it would be free to move out the open doors.

Then she started on her task. So slowly had she to move, with constant pauses to regain her failing strength, that it was halfway to dawn when she finally touched a match to the straw in the first barn. Then, stopping only for a moment to see a bright glow spreading, she started on her descent of the path to the valley. Not once did she look back. Had she, her eyes would have beheld a livid pillar of flame shooting high into the windy night, spreading to each of the three big barns. She heard shouting, and the sound of cars roaring along the highway. She was desperately tired now, tired and weak. She must rest, sleep.

Toward noon of the day following the fire, which had completely destroyed the three red barns on the farm, Orrin started down the hill path to see his mother, as he had told Dr. Derby he would do. In all the excitement after he had been called back from Cooperstown, arriving just in time to see the last of the barn walls collapse in red embers, he had forgotten everything else. Wondering what had prompted his stubborn old parent to this deathbed reconciliation, he shook his head and picked his way down the rocky path. A little over halfway down the hill, he found himself in a clump of sumac bushes. Turning to regain the path, he stumbled over what he at first thought was an old coat or a blanket flung across the way. He stooped close and froze in surprise. Huddled in the old woolen cloak was the frail body of his mother. With almost superhuman strength, Samantha had nearly made the shelter of her house before she died.

Almost from the day Orrin Randall returned from burying his mother to the blackened ruins of his great barns, his luck took a downward plunge. First a long drought in Cherry Valley blighted the crops. The wide alfalfa fields at Maple Ridge Farm, a vital source of income, withered on the stalk. The bank in Cooperstown where he was a director failed. Marsha died of hemorrhage bearing her second child, stillborn. Insomnia plagued the wretched man. He took to prowling in the valley at night, seeming to be drawn to the farm where he had grown up. Often passersby saw him sitting on the back porch of Samantha's house, which was now his, smoking, brooding all through the night.

A young farmhand, Yerbe Nelson, from the Talmadge place nearby, was returning home from a Halloween party. He took a short cut through the valley, passing close to the big gray barn. Startled by a light glowing in Justin's old workshop, Nelson stealthily looked through the cobwebbed pane of glass that served as a window. There, in an old barrel chair, sat proud, cold-eyed Orrin Randall, once the richest farmer in the county. The man was smoking a pipe and staring into space. Nelson told Talmadge next morning, "The look in Randall's eyes scared the daylights out'n me, for sure. Like a crazy man. He was all hunched over. His eyes were bloodshot. Empty whiskey bottles stood on the table beside him."

A year passed. Bad luck clung to Orrin Randall like cockleburs to the fetlocks of a farm horse. Then, one morning, it was discovered that he had disappeared. For nearly a week, the countryside was combed. All his old haunts were searched. Then someone suggested that the old Randall place, untenanted since Samantha's death, should be reopened and gone over thoroughly. The first floor yielded no clue. Then one of the searchers sniffed the air. "Come on upstairs," he called out to his helpers. There, in a room once occupied by Seth and Orrin Randall as growing boys, was the body of the master of Maple Ridge Farm, hanging from a rafter. The neck was encircled by a leather halter strap. Orrin had kicked a wooden stool from under his heavy boots.

The narrators of the countryside have a field day telling of apparitions haunting the old Randall place. Samantha is observed in broad daylight, clad in faded-blue print and sunbonnet. She still prods an invisible goose with her famous forked stick.

I saw her, one hot afternoon, standing in the shade of the doorway to the barn, which now sags so at every joint that it is on the verge of total collapse. The sunbonnet hid her features, but in the rigidity of her slab-sided body I recognized the fanatic purpose that enabled her, a fugitive from her deathbed, to climb the steep path to her ungodly son's farm and set his kingdom afire.

For a few years, a string of tenants—usually itinerant farmers, and once the proprietor of a gas station—tried to live in Samantha's house. But too many strangely upsetting things happened for comfort. I talked with the gas-station man.

"Myself, I didn't mind so much, but my womenfolk and the kids went near crazy," he said.

"Tell me what you, or they, saw," I said.

"Well, a woman in a blue dress and sunbonnet just can't seem to leave the place. At night, she stands in an upstairs bedroom just starin' at the ceilin'. Once or twice, my wife's sister said she saw a man hangin' from a rafter by his neck and the woman standin' sorta gloatin'. I don't know about that. I never saw it.''

Samantha is apparently a restless ghost, forever walking her acres. But then she was restless in life, doing the same thing. I have a conviction that it is her ghostly love for the old silvery moss-rimed barn that keeps it standing at all. I have painted it a number of times. Its singularly luminous patina of color alone is a challenge to any painter.

Brickbat Charlie and Razzmatazz

NATCHEZ-UNDER-THE-HILL, MISSISSIPPI, 1879

AMERICA in its birth pains brought forth some extraordinary tracts of human habitation: the Barbary Coast, of booming, gold-crazy San Francisco; the Bowery, of once staid, Dutch-colonized New Amsterdam; New Orleans, Bourbon and Rampart Streets; Chicago's Loop. In many cities, there were red-light quarters, where girls were born in whoredom and lived and died without ever leaving it.

Every growing city had its stews, but none could produce anything to compare with a settlement of dingy shacks—stucco, corrugated tin, and rotting timber—called Natchez-Under-the-Hill. Like a superating sore, this sinkhole lay along a narrow strip on the shore of the Mississippi, that old python of a river that sludges its way from the northern reaches of Minnesota through half a continent. The highest point of land along this riverway is found in the bluffs of Natchez. From the river wharves of Under-the-Hill, a road winds steeply up to the elegance of Natchez. Today it is one of the foremost points for pilgrimages to view the famous houses of the area—Rosalie, Melmont, D'Evereux, Melrose, and Dunleith.

In the days of Brickbat Charlie and his ripsnorting hellion of a consort, Hungarian Razzmatazz, probably no greater contrast in two neighboring habitations

107

could be found on the face of the globe than Natchez under, and Natchez atop, the hill. The alleys of the former ran blood from morning to night. One debauch took place on the exhausted carcass of another. Every known gyp game and vice, raw or gilded, flourished. The dead bodies of rivermen, gamblers, and unwary travelers were allowed to clog the backwash where they toppled or were thrown. On the bluff, the town was coolly shaded by magnolia, mimosa, and tulip trees. The pungent, aristocratic odor of box gardens drifted into ornamented drawing rooms in classically porticoed houses of rose and yellow brick.

Swarms of blood-gorged, poisonous flies ate at the faces of birth-diseased babies in the shacks of Under-the-Hill. Flies were not tolerated on the bluffs, where liveried black boys swung gilded, exotically decorated punkahs to and fro over dinner tables loaded with delicacies.

It was considered vastly daring for a young man to take his waltz partner out for a breath of air, then whisk her to the balustrade of a walk along the bluffs, there to gaze down into the phantasmagoria of iniquity below. Raucous shrieks and brassy music could be heard. If the wind was right, a stench of carrion and excrement drifted up to Paradise, as the bluffs were derisively called by those who lived below them. After a few shudders, the adventurers would run back to the safety and luxury of fragrant damask-hung rooms. Ironically, the bluffs of Natchez, half suffocated in politesse behind its fanlight doorways, existed between two murder traps. For a nearby back road of commerce and travel called Natchez Trace was the haunt of every kind of desperado.

This, then, was the state of affairs in Natchez in the year 1870, when Rose Mataz stepped off a riverboat and met Irish Charlie Dorsey, widely known among the river roisterers as Brickbat, for his prowess in hurling lethal bricks at all and sundry when he was drunk.

When Rose Mataz came off the river packet Palmyra Queen onto the slimy wharf boards of Natchez-Under-the-Hill, she was a stranger to anyone in the town sober enough to see her. Later that night, she told Charlie Dorsey, over glass after glass of redeye whiskey, the story of her life. It may or may not be true.

Rose was born Rozika Mataz in a village in the Hungarian Puszta. Tending the geese and swine on her father's farm did not appeal to her. One day, when she was in her fourteenth year, her father took his strapping daughter to a market fair in Debrecen. Left to hold the horse while her father bartered, blond, richly curved Rozika drew the attention of a horse-dealer from Buda Pest. In no time, he had made the girl a proposition that, while she did not fully understand the words, she liked hearing. "Silk dresses," "jewels," "dancing," and "theatres" sounded like music. She dropped the halter rope. That night she spent in the arms of the horse-dealer on a couch in a brothel in Buda. Mares and fillies like strong, country-bred Rozika were the stock in trade of this dealer.

Later, the girl joined a traveling circus. She waltzed with a Carpathian bear. She rode bareback dressed in a red-and-gold hussar uniform, which showed to perfection her firm, curved thighs. Soon she was appearing in Paris in a winter circus, and then it was America and peddling dope on the river steamers.

Because Rose, as she was now called, had consorted with gamblers for years, she had picked up many an unusual trick. Always dressed in high fashion, gaudy as a parrot, the woman cut a dashing figure, with terrific appeal for raffish males who like their women colorful and passionate.

Now, in her thirty-fifth year, Rose Mataz was a thoroughly bad lot let loose upon the world. She was, into the bargain, a mighty attractive bit of goods in a stridently flamboyant way. She was evil, treacherous in any dealing, and predatory as a vixen in heat. Added to this, Rose was bored. She walked into the first saloon that swung a door in her face. Scarcely was she inside the smoke-blue tunnel than a huge hand, like the paw of the Carpathian bear she had waltzed with, and as hairy, grabbed her around her corseted waist. A huge, evil-smelling brute with long black hair—almost like an Indian, she thought—swooped her into an alcove and onto the floor. That was the beginning.

Charlie Dorsey had reeked of bad whiskey as early as when he suckled at his drunken mother's breast in the purlieus of Goggin's Quay, along the Liffey in Dublin. By his tenth year, he had become adept at picking pockets and could remove a silver-buckled shoe from the foot of a nobleman as he raised it to cross a garbage-cluttered street. But Charlie, tired of evading the guards, stowed away on a ship leaving the Liffey Basin for London; from there by nefarious stages he found himself handling the sweeps of a flatboat on the Mississippi.

For a few years, this occupation sufficed. Charlie had all he could manage of the two things that were the breath of life to him—whiskey and women. The lower in instincts the woman was, the better she got on with Charlie. Finally, he drifted to Natchez-Under-the-Hill. After a few months of alcoholic stupor, Charlie realized that this bourne was his—if one dare use the expression—spiritual home.

So, in effect, there stood Satan, grinning in triumph, with arms spread wide apart. In one hand he held Charlie, hurler of brickbats; in the other Rose Mataz, Jezebel of the world. Satan chuckled. What a fusing for evil these two would make.

For a while after the arrival of Rose, she and Charlie just drowned themselves in lechery and liquor. Then, one night, they rowed across the river to the quiet town of Vidalia to rob a sugar overseer against whom Charlie had a grudge. The upshot was defeat. Both the potential bandits were too drunk to be cautious. Charlie hurled bricks, then a knife, cutting the head of the overseer wide open. A term in the Vidalia jail not only gave the two time to think soberly but to plan for future partnership.

After six months, the jail sentence served, Charlie and Rose resumed their disreputable life Under-the-Hill, but with new ideas. The two leopards had not changed their spots by enforced sobriety—far from it. If anything, the spots were larger. Now it was to be an anchored showboat on which lascivious skits and tableaux would be performed to entertain the avid appetites of the town's floating—in every sense of the word—population. During her stay in jail, Rose had gone over all her talents in the field of theatrical entertainment. She could waltz with a bear, dance solo, ride bareback, sing, juggle, and perform obscene acrobatic tricks. There was no reason, both agreed, why the showboat—Razzmatazz, as they proposed to call the venture—should not be the sensation of the entire Mississippi Valley. It was.

On a spring night of soft breezes, when the settlement of Under-the-Hill was fairly bursting at the seams with visitors, the gaudily painted front of a wooden theatre, built on board an anchored mud scow, was lighted with tallow dips in colored glass globes. Huge red letters proclaimed to the few who could read:

SHOWBOAT RAZZMATAZZ
BRICKBAT CHARLIE AND ROSE MATAZ

EXTRAVAGANZA
Music
Dancing

Admission Two Dollars—Liquor Extra

Both Charlie and Rose, being unable to read, thought this lettered sign very elegant. Each had learned the words by heart. They never tired of quoting it to onlookers, quickly and easily, as if reading it for the first time.

The venture was a resounding success from the start. Twice within a year, Rose, who was the business head and kept reasonably sober these days, raised the price of admission and of liquor served to patrons. Her costumes were fantasies of red, orange, purple, and green, with yards of tinsel and towering head-dresses of brilliant but molting plumage. For herself, she kept pretty well covered, choosing her style of costume from the Moulin Rouge, in Paris, where she had once danced in the ensemble. But the twelve girls who sang as a chorus while she was changing were almost naked, and the bits of ribbon or satin they did wear on their bodies were soon torn off by the rampaging members of the audience. Charlie, never quite sober, took money at the door, acted as bouncer, and even essayed a strong-man act in yellow tights. But the rivermen, who were as strong as he was, yelled him off the stage. A few brickbats were thrown, a few knifings let blood, and Charlie went back to the cash cubby and bouncing.

The Razzmatazz continued to prosper. Its reputation for baudy lawlessness swung up and down the river. Even slumming parties from Vicksburg, Tallulah, and Alexandria paid the place at least one visit.

Then, in pure greed for higher profits, Rose played a stupid hand. She began cutting the liquor with river water. Next, she raised the prices again, this time of everything in sight. It cost a man twenty dollars a throw to take a show-boat girl into one of the couch-furnished alcoves. So the act was done outside in the alleys, or in the bushes, for far less.

Meanwhile, life in the red-brick house at the end of Locust Walk, the best house in town, which Rose had bought with the first profits, resounded to quarrels of furious intensity. On mornings after Rose and Charlie got back from a night of salooning, bedlam broke loose. Charlie would bellow some unintelligible obscenity in his thick voice. Rose would shout in return, "Shut your god-damned mouth before I keep my promise to kill you! Go away from me, you dirty old alligator!" And then, on a higher note, "And give back the money you stole from the till. I saw you. I suppose you gave it to Daisy, didn't you? Well, let me tell you . . ." And so it raged until both were too weary to continue.

Then one day, just when the seams were beginning to split wide open in the life of Rose and Charlie, a long-faced corpse-like individual came walking down the hill road from the bluffs. In appearance, he was shadier than any of the denizens in this outpost to Hell. He might easily have been the original jay in the song sung by Rose and her girls—one of her milder renditions.

There came one day a pious jay,
A jay with a red goatee.
I winked at him, he beckoned me
This jay with the red goatee.
He ended up in the morgue on ice,
But I rolled him first for something nice,
This jay with the red goatee-e-e
This jay with the red goatee.

The name of the jay was Jepson Strutter. He coughed delicately behind his hand, snapped his tiny red-rimmed pig's eyes, and smiled at Rose. "I am one of the Strutters—of Strutter's boys, you know. A silent partner, you might say. The gentleman of the bunch. I"—again he coughed deprecatingly—"spy out the land."

Always on the lookout for profit, Rose mused. Pouring her guest a glass of redeye she surveyed the piazza of her brick house. Yes, it wanted doing up. Getting a bit run down. She regarded Strutter coldly. "Why tell me all this? Do you want another silent partner? I know everybody on the river. Come inside, we'll talk about it."

Up and down the Natchez Trace, the name "Strutter's boys" brought cold, stark fear clutching at the heart. In twenty years, this band of thieves and cutthroats had burned and pillaged more outlying farms, usually murdering the owners, than any of the elusive bands of outlaws then plying up and down the unfrequented roads along the Mississippi. Rafe Strutter, a tawny-haired giant with the cruelty of an Apache Indian, was the ringleader. Four brothers and a collection of cousins, nephews, and besotted hangers-on made up a band loosely numbered at thirty men. From time to time, the notorious Langley band lay in ambush for their rivals, or the Strutters paid the same compliment to the Langleys. Sometimes an open battle took place in the clearings that dotted the thickly grown, miasma-drenched Trace. Most of the time, Strutter's boys held forth supreme in the reign of terror along the Trace.

Little by little, it was borne home to the whiskey-dulled mind of Charlie Dorsey that Rose was mighty prosperous. Business on the Razzmatazz was about as usual, but she was different. The house on Locust Walk was refurnished from cellar to garret. Rose no longer appeared nightly in the show. Sometimes she would depart for a trip up or down the river. She never told anybody where. She would suddenly return, newly upholstered with all the silks and velvets and furs she could carry. Jewels, too. Real sparklers. This took money. Even Charlie knew that.

One night, Rose returned unexpectedly to the brick house. It was an ill-starred return. She found Charlie in bed with Daisy, a girl from the showboat, an octoroon of voluptuous beauty. The fight that ensued woke even Under-the-Hill from its blasé indifference to such affairs. Still dressed in yellow and purple satin from her journey, Rose grabbed a rawhide bull whip frequently used by Charlie on his slaves. Up the narrow street of the town she chased the naked, shrieking girl, crosshatching the hide of her back and buttocks in runnels of blood.

After the night of the whip-lashing, blows of adversity fell upon Rose thick and fast. First, her confederate, sleazy Jepson Strutter, fumbled a kidnapping for ransom that involved the young son of a prominent Natchez banker. Jepson was caught and jailed in the upper town.

Meanwhile, in revenge for the whipping of his paramour, Charlie set out for the blood of Rose, of whom he was mightily tired. That she had partially gouged out one of his eyes in the fracas did not subtract from his hate. He staggered into the house late one night and accused her of working with the Strutter gang and keeping all the profits. "I'll see you hung, you slut! I'll go up to Paradise and tell the judge." Mumbling and swaying, he reached for a jug of red-eye. "Come mornin' thas what I'll do."

But come morning brickbat-hurling Charlie Dorsey was a smoking carcass drifting down the muddy Mississippi in a dugout canoe.

When Charlie, reeling and slobbering across the room, threatened Rose with exposure, she realized the game was up. He might forget all about it when his hazy mind cleared; then again he might not. The chance was not worth taking. Rose knew that the citizens of Natchez were roused to indignation as never before by the brazen attempt at kidnapping. She also knew that if she was arrested, it would mean a long sentence. Jepson, who might keep still if she was not exposed, would doubtless spill everything if she was.

Rose looked angrily at the huge, gross figure snoring on the bed. "Charlie's got to go," she said. "And tonight."

The clock on the mantel struck three o'clock. She had only two hours until first dawn; soon after that it would be full sunup. Rose Mataz, from the time of her bolt with the white-slaver in the market place of Debrecen, had made many a quick getaway. Up to now, her exits had not included murder. She turned again and looked at Charlie. He was so big to handle. Well, the Devil was kind —Charlie was dead drunk.

For an hour, every move Rose made was sure, executed with dispatch. She put on a dark dress. She wadded a large cache of goldbacks and jewels into a satchel and slung it by a strap over her shoulder. Grasping the lead-weighted handle of the rawhide whip in both hands, she dealt Charlie Dorsey a sudden savage blow on the head, then another, and, in quick succession, a few more. He snorted and jerked convulsively a few times, then lay inert. Rose wrapped his smashed skull with a tablecloth, and fetched a handcart from the garden. She mustered all her strength and loaded the dead weight into the cart, then pushed it down to the inlet at the back of the garden. It did not matter now how many clues she left. By morning-coffee time, she would be well away. The steamy stench of this rotten hole of Under-the-Hill had seen the last of her.

She needed two boats—the little skiff and the wooden dugout canoe, both anchored in the inlet. She also needed a can of coal oil and some matches. When all was ready, Rose tore the scene of Charlie's murder to pieces. She broke bottles and smeared the bloody tablecloth around the room until it looked as if an unholy fight had taken place.

At the water's edge, Rose tied the dugout to the skiff with a slack rope. Then, poling swiftly, she steered the grisly cargo out into the swift current. For about an hour she poled, keeping the two crafts in mid-river. A wide, flat wood barge, with two men at the sweeps, sped past her. One of them called, "Hullo thar, Cindy! Whar you goin' to tie up fer tonight?" She waved and nodded.

About two hours after sunup, Rose eased the boats out of the current and into a backwater where the forest grew down to the water. Dark, steaming caves of green foliage hid her from the river. The woman worked slowly now. Maneuvering the dugout into the water under a bank, she leaned over and emptied the can of coal oil over the body of Charlie, then untied the two boats.

For a few minutes, Rose hesitated. Then, suddenly she struck a match, threw it onto the flannel-shirted shoulder, and let go the canoe rope. A spurt of hot flame shot out. Hastily she moved her skiff out of the tunnel of greenery and was soon lost in the reaches of midstream.

Three days later, a heavy storm lashed the river valley. The waters of the old python rolled and churned, beating into strong waves in the backwaters.

Then one day soon afterward, some boys on a raft, out fishing for bullheads, saw a log floating down the river. It passed close by the raft. "Oh, lookee, thar's a dead man thar!" yelled one boy, pointing to the blackened mass. "No," said another, "tain't nuther. It's a ole charred log. Look, they's a water rat aridin' on it. Cain yo hit 'im?" The boy shied a tin can at the rat. The varmint, out of reach, went on gnawing.

Rose left the river at Donaldsonville, above New Orleans, during the storm that set the half-consumed body of Charlie Dorsey afloat. Some of her last mysterious trips had been to New Orleans, where her garish toilettes had been remarked; it was just as well she was not seen there for a time. By coach and fruit steamer, she reached Galveston. It was too hot and she was restless. San Antonio, Fort Worth, Dallas. She soon tired of them all. She tried taking a chair in the parlor of a famous sporting house in San Antonio. But the men always passed her up for younger, gayer girls. Rose was used to being top attraction. "The hell with these old goats," she said to the Madam. Soon, gaudily dressed, she plied her trade on the streets.

A year or so after Rose had so bloodily left Under-the-Hill, she emerged from a stagecoach one evening in the rousing town of Oklahoma City, a city of brightly lighted saloons and boarding houses. The houses had high peaked false fronts, which were painted chocolate and sapphire blue and olive green and showed tall bay windows draped in Nottingham-lace curtains. "This," said Rose, "is the place for me. Here I can hit my stride."

Within a month, Rose Mataz had bought a three-story house on the main street. She hocked her jewels, or most of them, to do it. A few showy ones she kept for display on her plump throat and for the proverbial rainy day. The house was raspberry red combined with an elegant gray trim. Nottingham lace caught back with raspberry satin bows gave passersby a tantalizing glimpse of the pretty face and lightly veiled bosom of one of the bevy of young women who entertained in this handsome edifice. Rose called it Paradise, in memory, perhaps, of the town on the bluffs of the Mississippi.

For a number of years, Rose was Madam of the most luxurious brothel in town. Her girls were always fresh and congenial. Every hidden vice was catered to. Indeed, Madam Rose's Paradise was "Paradise enow."

As the prosperous years dovetailed, one into another, Rose followed the pattern of women of her kind. She bought stalwart lovers. As she aged and grew immensely fat, she picked them always younger. She drank increasingly. Straight gin was her tipple, a formidable brew when taken in excess. Rose knew, toward the last, that her girls were robbing her right and left. Knew her young lovers lived with girls of their own on her money. The same old story.

"Old sot," she heard herself referred to. "Old hag."

In her seventieth year, alone in her big, satiny bed, Rose Mataz died. Satan held out his hand to her. Old battered Rose took it gratefully, for she was ready to go.

One night—a brilliant moonlight night—at the turn of the century, a jailer at the ivy-hung jail of Vidalia stopped suddenly outside the bars of a cell that was supposed to be empty. It wasn't. On the narrow wooden bunk sat a golden-haired woman. She was dressed in a bright-red gown, with an immodestly low-cut bodice and a huge flaring bustle. She seemed oblivious to the startled man outside in the corridor. She hummed a tune and then took a smooth pointed stick from her girdle and proceeded to clean her nails. The jailer sped down the corridor to his office and called a friend who had dropped by for a drink. When the two men returned, the cell was empty.

After that, whenever this particular cell was unoccupied by a prisoner, it was occupied by the ghost of Rose Mataz. She got to be quite a pet around the jail. One old man even remembered that as a young lawyer he had been in the courtroom at Vidalia the day Charlie Dorsey and Rose Mataz had been sentenced for attempted robbery and knifing. People in Vidalia did not put up with shenanigans as they did in that hellhole across the river. The woman Rose had worn a bright-red dress with a bustle.

It would seem that one of the few times in her tempestuous life when Rose Mataz had been let alone to think in complete sobriety, with no demands whatsoever on her person, had been the months in Vidalia jail. In effect, her ghost returned to this scene to take a rest cure.

Young Man in a Coonskin Cap

BRANDYWINE CREEK, DELAWARE, 1805

STUDENTS of ghost stories have long been intrigued by lycanthropy, the belief—named by the Attic Greeks—that men and women could turn themselves into wolves or foxes, resuming human form at will. Dark tales of werewolves still form a strong pattern in the lives of inhabitants of the Balkan countries, and have spread in various forms all over the world. However, except in Mittel-europa, it is the fox more than the wolf that appears in stories of the supernatural.

A red dog fox, which may or may not be Gil Thoreau, the coon-skin crowned young man whose father was a scout for General Lafayette, is seen slinking in the byways of Delaware and Pennsylvania and as far north as stately Manoir Le Ray, at Le Raysville, near Watertown, New York. Sometimes the figure of Thoreau is observed a short while before or after the fox. No one has ever reported meeting the two together, as they were in life.

What seems to be a struggle for possession of gunpowder-making secrets plays an important role in the story. A theory has been put forward that Gil Thoreau was a spy in the pay of owners of the Du Pont Powder Mill, hired to watch Jacques de Chaumont, who had sent gunpowder to General Lafayette.

Actually, there seems to have been little need to spy on the de Chaumonts. Whatever the reason was, however, a de Chaumont brought about Gil's death.

His subsequent return is, to my mind, one of the most diverting tales of the Revolutionary period.

When the French ship L'Aventurier from Brest put in at Newport, Rhode Island, in the spring of 1800, three distinguished passengers walked down the gangplank—Samuel du Pont de Nemours and his sons Irenée and Victor. Irenée was a student of the famous chemist Lavoisier, whose zeal had caused him to be guillotined during the Terror.

Thomas Jefferson, a man of vision, had met the elder du Pont de Nemours in France. Knowing that America needed a good grade of gunpowder, Jefferson invited the three men to emigrate. They did so, and their first mill for experimentation was located on Brandywine Creek. The spot was isolated; there was plenty of room to engage in testing the range of gunpowder-discharged mortar balls.

When the du Ponts went ashore at Newport, they became conscious of the hovering presence of an unusual-looking individual who seemed to be scarcely out of his teens. Shabby homespun garments hung on his spare frame. His thatch of blue-black hair was crowned by an immense coonskin cap, with tail trailing down his back. He was a type of fellow seen every day in the American colonies, but to the newly arrived Frenchmen he was an arresting, even a puzzling, sight. Each time the du Ponts looked at him, the youth grinned in a completely engaging manner and touched his coonskin with a lean brown hand.

"Is he an Indian?" asked Victor of his guide.

"Laws, no," the man said, and laughed. "That's Gil Thoreau. He's your guide down to Brandywine. He takes you on where I leaves off."

A deep, far-reaching friendship was formed between the three du Ponts and the shy, gangling youth who at that time was already a noted scout and guide. Gil told them about his early life. The story came out piecemeal, for he was no raconteur, over the crossed-log fires built nightly at the mill, where temporary barracks had been built to shelter the du Ponts and the workmen. He could barely remember his mother. She had come from Maryland, down Havre de Grace way. She died when he was only a tucket. What was that? Gill grinned widely. "That's a kid that still has to be tucked in a trundle at night. Three year ole or so."

Of his father, Pierre, he had a clear memory, little of it good. The man had come down from Chicoutimi, on the Saguenay, to offer his services as scout to General Lafayette. He became a woods runner, for he had great endurance and a slippy way of covering distance in the enemy-filled forests. Delivery of important letters from one general to another was entrusted to him.

But the trustworthiness of Pierre's character ceased with his role of messenger. A bad lad in every other respect, he was exceedingly devious with liquor, women, and money. Brawls and knifings in low taverns and whore dens filled his days when he was not on active duty. His wife died of grief and abuse, leaving a small son. For a few years, the boy, Gil, followed his father from place to place, lonely and often beaten. Then, one terrifying night, the remote farmhouse where Gil was being boarded out was attacked by hostile Mohawks. All the occupants of the homestead were massacred, and little Gil, aged ten years, was carried off to the Indian camp. Strange to relate, the boy was treated as the son of the chief.

As Gil told it, "I didn't rightly know why I wasn't whipped or made to work. One day, after I picked up some Mohawk lingo, I was told by an old squaw that the chief wanted a son and I was it. 'Pears the chief's boys had all been killed and he was too old for more. So I learned all their scoutin' ways. Now I know the woods and how to live off it, good as any Indian. Yes, sir. My name is French-Canuck, rightly. Guillaume—that's why I'm called Gil."

During the War of 1812, when du Pont black powder won decisive battles for the American army, Gil Thoreau disappeared from the Brandywine for long periods. Sometimes, in the night, he would knock on the door of the stone house that had been built by Irenée du Pont near Wilmington. The visitor would be quickly admitted, curtains pulled and windows shuttered, and then the occupants of the house would sit until dawn in close conversation. When daylight approached, the tall, deeply bronzed young man in the coonskin cap, which he wore winter and summer, would step outside and be gone.

Sometime during this period Gil picked up a red-fox cub. Passing close to a stone wall one evening, somewhere near Oneida Lake, he came upon a crudely constructed snare; in it was a fox cub struggling to get loose. Gil freed him, looked for broken bones, and, finding none, slipped the trembling cub into a wide pocket of his deerskin jacket. From then on, the two were never separated. Gil named his little companion Fiery. The varmint learned amusing tricks as fast as Gil could teach him. For travel, Fiery was taught to lie around the back of Gil's neck, head and legs on Gil's shoulders; this was an excellent mode of conveyance when Gil traveled swiftly through the forests.

A few years after the War of 1812, Gil Thoreau was almost shot by one of the de Chaumonts at Le Ray. Whether or not he was spying is not known. At any rate, a group of windowless stone buildings on the property seemed to interest the scout immensely. While trying to gain entrance to what he may have thought was a gunpowder repository, he was surprised by a man who appeared around the corner of a building carrying a shotgun. The man flashed a lantern at Gil, dropped it, and aimed his gun. Gil, schooled in the tricks of the savages who had reared him, threw himself flat on the ground. Grasping the foot of the man, he upset him and the gun exploded in the air. But Gil had seen the face of Jacques de Chaumont in the upflare cast by the lanthorn. Quickly he made his escape into the nearby shadows.

When Gil returned to Brandywine, he was closeted for a long time with Victor du Pont. One can imagine the gist of the talk. Why, if there was nothing in the story of stored gunpowder—whether to sell to the government or to be used in research—was a group of stone buildings resembling arsenals so carefully guarded by the lord of the manoir himself? One can also imagine that the spying—if it *was* that—continued.

Once, and only once, does romance with a woman enter the story of the young man in the coonskin cap. Near the Brandywine lived a farmer named Carrol and his daughter Selthy. She was a charmer with many beaux, but she had eyes for only one man, Gil Thoreau, though he was often "here today and gone tomorrow." Selthy was a prize, for not only did her looks beguile but when her father died, she would inherit a fine farm.

The shy Gil pondered. He was thirty-five years old. Long nights in damp forests were beginning to tell. His joints ached some mornings. Well, he'd give it a try. But when Gil stated to Selthy that Fiery was as much a part of himself as his right hand, and he must be regarded as such, a storm broke. As Gil told it to Victor du Pont, "There was one hell of a row. She snatched at Fiery to throw him out the door. He bit her on the shoulder. Won't be no marryin' now."

After the upset to his matrimonial plans, Gil slipped away again. Travelers from Pennsylvania or upstate New York arriving at Brandywine told of meeting him or glimpsing his figure far off on the skyline—lonely, loping Gil Thoreau with a red fox, full-grown now, lying peacefully across his shoulders. One Conestoga wagon driver told, in Klister's Ordinary, "I seen this here scout Gil Thoreau. Hot as tophet noonday 'twas, nigh about Skaneateles Lake, and he was takin' steps a league long, singin' at the top of his lungs. Don't know where he was bound, nor why. He looked all fur. Big coonskin cap and red fox critter layin' across his back. Cussedest youngun I ever did see."

"He hain't no youngun no more," drawled a man, over his whiskey mug. "Forty-five, or about. But he looks like a kid, darnation if he don't."

And so Gil Thoreau and Fiery went along the hills and valleys. The mighty mountains of the Appalachian Range knew them. The Mohawk River Valley, with its great vistas of timbered foothills and misted peaks reaching to the clouds, sheltered him.

Then one moonlight night in the midsummer, when Gil was fifty years old, he staggered into the compound surrounding the du Pont testing field on the Brandywine, and fell at the door of the Foreman's room. Dirty blood-crusted bandages were loosely wound across his right shoulder, in which a deep knife wound, many days old, had turned green. Below his heart gaped two bullet holes. When water was brought, he just managed to murmur, "Le Ray . . . Chaumont," and died.

Later, as Gil was being laid out, one of the men who had come to help said, "First time I seen Gil without that critter Fiery round his neck or on his knee. First time ever."

Naturally, whenever a red fox is seen coursing the fields and woodland paths that were once the hunting grounds of Gil Thoreau, there is no reason to suppose it is Gil practising lycanthropy. Strange tales are told, however, by walkers in the woods and fields of a red fox suddenly appearing on the path. Paying no attention to any human, the fox speeds silently past, its pads making no sound upon the hard earth. Then—perhaps a few hundred yards, maybe a mile, farther along—the deerskin-clothed figure of a tall, thin young man wearing a huge coonskin cap will lope into view. He, too, will pass silently, eyes intent on the trail ahead.

In the days when the Erie Canal was a popular and pleasant way to travel from Albany to Buffalo, many voyagers related tales of seeing the ghost of Gil Thoreau. At a distance ran Fiery.

A woman journalist from Richmond, Virginia, diverting herself by water travel in the North, wrote this paragraph in her journal, "Yankee Pleasure Ways":

"I boarded the canal barge Mohawk Chief at Albany. We set out in a blaze of sunrise. We passed green farmlands and pretty, tree-clustered villages. The dragonflies and wild birds made darting color in the sunlight. The day turned hot; I was forced to retire to rest. At evening we tied up at a small hamlet, and I sat late on deck to enjoy the cool air. The moon rose behind the fringe of trees bordering the canal. I was about to gather my shawls and retire when I saw a fox padding noiselessly along the towpath. I could have leaned over and touched Master Renard, so close was he. I was not frightened in the least, for, oddly, the fox seemed scarcely real. The canal swung to the right a few yards away, and as my eyes followed the path of the fox, he seemed to melt into the moonlight. Turning to pursue my intention to retire, I was again confounded. Now it was the figure of a man of extraordinary appearance. Too tall to be real, he wore Indian fringes and a fur cap. As silently as the fox had stolen past me, this spectral figure did likewise. What held my attention was the fact that though the landscape was bathed in brightest moonlight, the apparition, for I am convinced it was such, cast no shadow on the towpath."

At Le Ray, the beautiful country mansion of Jacques de Chaumont, there occurred a plague of foxes in which barnyard fowl were molested and carried off. A lone red fox was seen sitting on the lawn in front of the portico. For hours, the animal would remain motionless, watching. Whenever he was approached, the sentinel fox melted away, only to return. On nights of the full moon, he would bark in a most frenzied manner; in the morning, blood was found splattered on the white steps of Le Ray.

ROCK-BOUND COAST COLLECTION

NEW ENGLAND

The Slavering Hound

PORTSMOUTH, NEW HAMPSHIRE

Among the data on American ghost lore that I have collected myself from time to time or that have been told to me when a group of people have been discussing the supernatural, I find a great many short jottings. To me, some have a compelling core, a stark, primitive quality. Here are four of them.

A SHARP BREEZE blew across the jetty from the east. "Couldn't rightly call it a blow yet," remarked Sarah Olcott to Tibby, her tiger cat, lying on the doorsteps intent on the eternal feline tongue bath. "Better tie up my hollyhocks just the same. Never know, way out here, when a blow'll come."

As Mrs. Olcott was about to untangle a handful of raffia strands from a peg beside the kitchen door, she heard a shout rise above the wind. Looking toward the road on the mainland, where the fishing boats were tied, she gave a wave to young Seth Parkins, who was calling to her through a megaphone.

"Can ye hear me, Miz Olcott? I got a telephone message for you."

"Yes, I can hear you!" Sarah called, through cupped hands. "Go ahead."

In loud, deep tones, which Seth, aged fourteen years, imagined were very grown up, he delivered: "Miss Mary Lawrence and two women will be a mite late gettin' here today. Had trouble with machine. Don't wait supper. They'll eat on road. Be here probably 'bout ten o'clock. Get all that?" The boy's voice cracked as he shouted the question. The woman nodded, waved her apron, and went back to tying up her hollyhocks. Well, that was a little disappointing, she thought. After I cooked a real good dinner for them, too. Can't be helped though. Hope they ain't *too* late.

Sarah Olcott's house stood at the end of a peninsula of rocky land that ran out into the sea for about an eighth of a mile. The peninsula, which was made up of piled rocks with a sand road laid on top, had been built by her late husband's grandfather, Trubee Olcott, about 1810, so that his house and lobster pens and gratings would be away from the constant comings and goings of the fishing fleet at Boynton, an arm of fishermen's houses along a wooden wharf flung out from Portsmouth. The house was built of stone and brick, unusual to find in this seacoast shanty colony. Trubee Olcott had wanted a good, warm, wind-defying house in which to raise his family.

Now Sarah Olcott, who had been born Daniels, from Portsmouth, lived in the house alone. In the summer, she sometimes took a few carefully chosen and well-referenced boarders—always women. Mostly they were schoolteachers or office workers from Boston or Concord or Rutland. Once, she'd had a nice actress from New York. The house was comfortable, with everything modern except that she had no telephone. She had a dynamo for her electricity, and her supply of fresh water was ample. It was the garden, walled on three sides to ward off the wind, that occupied most of her time and interest. The lobster business, her sole means of livelihood except her occasional boarders, she let out to the Bascome brothers.

About sunset, Sarah closed the double windows against the real blow she expected before morning and settled down with Tibby on her lap to wait for her guests to arrive. Every once in a while, she could hear a motor horn on the main road. There was a good deal of traffic in the summer on the coast road from Newburyport to Portland. After each horn-blowing, which she calculated was at Bugbee's garage, she allowed enough time for her visitors to walk along the causeway. But it got to be half-past eleven and no arrivals. Well, she'd wait until midnight. If they weren't here by then, she doubted they would show up before next forenoon.

Then she heard a horn blow four or five short blasts. So she settled back, stroking Tibby. In a few minutes now, she'd know. Suddenly Tibby straightened rigidly in her lap; every hair of her fur stood electrically charged with fear. Unsheathed claws dug painfully into Sarah's gingham-clad thighs, and with a wailing yell the cat leaped from her mistress's lap and streaked up the stairs like a bat out of Hell. "Mercy on us! What can have started Tibby off like that?" Sarah said to herself.

She hastened to the door to look down the road. Before she could slip the bolt out of its socket, a scream of terror ripped across the night. Then came another scream, in a different key, as if from another throat. Then another, until three voices, or so it seemed, shrieked in unholy fear.

Thrusting the door wide open, Sarah ran down the dooryard path toward the picket gate. Leaning over the top bar, she could just make out the figures of three women running madly in her direction. "What is it? What frightened you? Are you all right?" she called.

The women practically fell through the gate and rushed past Sarah into the front room. She followed them in and spent a long time calming them down. Finally, one of the women, Mary Lawrence, spoke. In a nervous voice, she told this story, prompted now and again by her friends.

"All day long, from the time we left Boston, bad luck rode with us. Helen Ryle drove for a time, then Lesley took over. Just outside of Newburyport, we had a blowout. After that, I drove, and as we neared Exeter, I had to detour through back roads and alleys. Then our rear axle cracked over a deep cut in the road. That's when I telephoned a message to you. Well," Mary said, "when we got to Portsmouth, it was half-past eleven and dark as a pocket. Finally, I found the Bugbee garage you wrote us about. I honked a few times and a boy came out. He took our bags out and told us to walk across the causeway. We couldn't miss your house, he said, because it was white and the only house out here. But none of us could see it, the night was so pitch black. When we were about halfway across, all holding on to each other, I, who was in the middle, saw an animal coming toward us. At first, I did not know what it was. Then I saw it was a hound-dog, head lowered, tongue hanging out."

Sarah Olcott was sitting bolt upright in her chair. She said, in a hushed voice, "Miss Lawrence, was the hound white? Did it have a long pointed muzzle?"

Mary thought for a minute. Helen Ryle nodded and said, "Yes, Mrs. Olcott. I could see the hound a long way off. Odd, I thought, too. We couldn't see your house, which is white, but we could see this dog way off. It sort of gleamed."

Lesley Tabor shuddered. "I can see it now, sort of bounding along. It had a pale-colored tongue, and it drooled onto the roadway."

Mary took up the tale. "The horrible part of it was that as the animal approached us, I expected it to turn aside, but no, it came straight at us. I had the impression it was looking at us balefully from under its brows. Without swerving an inch, it passed between Helen and me. That's when I screamed—we all screamed. It was awful. I turned to see where the creature would go, but there was no hound anywhere in sight. It made no sound. I can't remember hearing it when it passed between—almost through—us."

Sarah Olcott rose from her chair. "You have seen the phantom hound—or, as some around here call it, the slavering hound of Orbey's Neck. He's on the prowl tonight because the moon is full. Heavy clouds came up around ten o'clock. Before then, it was as bright as day. The hound comes out of the sea. That's why it gleamed—with phosphorus. I've seen it a good many times in my life. There'll be a death tomorrow. Not you. Somebody in Boynton or Portsmouth. It always happens that way. Let's go upstairs now. We'll see what we'll see in the morning."

When the three lodgers came downstairs next morning, buoyed up considerably by a night's rest and a fine, fair day to greet them, Sarah Olcott was not in the house. Helen Ryle went to a window and saw the woman standing at the farthest end of the peninsula, looking intently at something in the water. Since Helen's friends were in the kitchen getting breakfast started, she walked out and joined Mrs. Olcott. Following the older woman's gaze, she looked down among the rocks, and cried out in horror. There, rising and falling on the swell of sea-weed-clogged water, was the body of a young fisherman in blue dungarees and sweater. The man's throat had been ripped and torn, as if by the sharp teeth of a savage animal.

"It's Sam Weldon, one of the Portsmouth fishermen," said Sarah Olcott, in a toneless voice. "It's always the same. A young fisherman. That was Burr Orbey's curse."

Later, after the body of the fisherman had been taken away, Sarah told the three women the story of the slavering hound and the raging father's curse.

Somewhere around 1800, a man named Burr Orbey had come from London to live in a mansion out on the Dover road. He lived alone except for the occasional visits of Piers, his wild-living son. This young man would visit his father only when he was in need of funds. At other times, it was said, he lived in Boston or New York. Whenever he was at Orbey's Neck, as the house was called, he ranged the villages, looking for women. On one of his visits, he raped the wife of a young fisherman from Portsmouth. The woman was in delicate health and died from the effects of the rape. Crazed with grief, the husband swore he would kill Piers Orbey.

Often when Piers was staying with his father, he would take a small pinnace out into the semicircular bay near Olcott's jetty. Usually he was accompanied by a ferocious hound his father kept to frighten away intruders from Orbey's Neck. The hound was a peculiar breed of dog; no one had seen its like before. In size and shape, the animal resembled an English setter. It had a white body, with a small, pointed head, black as ink. The tail, long and plumy, was carried arched over the creature's back. What startled everyone who saw the hound was the odd way it held its head down, as if to spring, and the constant slavering of the tongue.

A few nights after the death of the fisherman's wife, Piers Orbey, companioned by his hound, set off in the pinnace for a sail in the full glory of a moonlight night. A small dory, which he did not see, set out at the same time from the shelter of some rocks near the jetty. The boat was a randan, propelled by three rowers, a swift and silent means of navigation. One can only surmise what took place when the three men, one the bereaved husband, slipped alongside the pinnace. The next morning, the pinnace was found drifting on the Boynton rocks; Piers' body lay in the boat.

"Death by strangulation," the coroner stated in his report. No trace of the hound was found.

When the old recluse Burr Orbey was told what had happened, he claimed the body of his dead son, and, standing over it, shouted, "I will have vengeance among the fishermen of Boynton and Portsmouth! They shall be struck down in the full of the moon! My hound shall be my avenger!"

"So," Sarah said, shaking her head, "many's the fisherman who's paid with his life by having his throat torn out. And always someone sees the slavering hound on the prowl before the disaster."

Dusty Lace and Tortoise Shell

NARRAGANSETT, RHODE ISLAND

SEEN from the street, the house built by Japhet Wedderburn in 1830 was much in plan like many other mansions built by wealthy sea captains in the China trade. The big square four-storied house of white clapboard, shuttered in dark green, was imposing yet dignified in its simplicity. No nonsense. The one feature with the least pretense to ornamentation was the handsome doorway. At the top of a flight of iron-railed steps, this Corinthian-columned recess was arched by a broken pediment centering a carved pineapple. A fanlight of pale-amethyst glass lent grace to the design.

The day Japhet returned from a long cruise and found the house almost finished, he rapped his blackthorn stick on the marble gatestone. In the voice he used for yelling orders from the bridge, he shouted to his builder, "I like it! The Sunset Cloud skims the water pretty. This house sets the land pretty. Now what I need here is a pretty woman to set in the house." He laughed raucously; Japhet was wondrous fond of his own jokes.

Until he should find the right woman, Japhet hired as housekeeper a woman from Narragansett whose family he had known all his life. Her name was Huldy Craddock, and she was a big-breasted female with narrow eyes and a talent for saving money. She knew her place, too. As Japhet told Luke Prentiss, his first mate, "Huldy won't try to creep into my bed when I ain't lookin'. But if I want her there, she'll come runnin'."

On the voyage after Japhet moved into his new house, he went not to China but to Tortuga and the Barbados. Just what he wanted in Tortuga, a godforsaken haunt of buccaneers and a few despoiled and dissolute Spanish families, caused speculation. No one was kept long in doubt.

When the raking hull of the Sunset Cloud, with its cargo of Barbados rum, tobacco, and sugar, tied up at the wharf, the Captain came down the gangway with a woman of evident Spanish birth on his arm. As persons remarked in the months and years that followed, it was the only time anyone ever saw the two together.

Escorted by her husband, Doña Mercedes entered the pineapple-crested door of the Wedderburn mansion, on Front Street. Huldy Craddock greeted her with a deep bow. The door closed. With the exception of the few times Doña Mercedes went out to do a bit of shopping during the first weeks after her arrival, she remained behind the white portals for years, unseen, unknown.

Soon after Japhet Wedderburn had ensconced his Spanish wife in his—for the times—luxuriously furnished house, he again went off to sea. For six years, the Captain spent less than five months at home, all told. When, later, he built a clipper ship—the Black Arrow, which he raced back and forth across the seas —he scarcely spent enough time in the house to know his way around.

In plan, the house was completely different from the big Georgian, Regency, and Federal houses built in shipping centers along the New England coast. Actually, the Wedderburn house was rather lopsided. Instead of the main stairway mounting from a hall in the center of the building, it rose against one entire side wall. Six windows, one above the other, mounted with the treads. As one reached the top of this staircase, there stretched a long gallery of a hallway, with eight tall windows, giving a superb view of the coast and the ever-restless Atlantic.

Huldy once said to a crony of hers, "It's like livin' in an aquarium. The way the sun pours into that upper hallway is enough to fade a block of granite. That's where *she* walks all the time, cryin' her eyes out." At that time, no one except Huldy and Japhet, on his rare visits, ever saw the lachrymose Doña Mercedes.

After a five-year period when Japhet had been home once, for a few weeks, Huldy said to a neighbor, over the drying-yard fence, "It's a shame, so it is. The poor woman is no more than a child. Why, she hardly comes up to my chest. Her hands and feet are like a doll's. If she didn't wear that high tortoise-shell comb and the black lace mantilla draped over it, she wouldn't even look grown up." Huldy smoothed down her apron. "I do all I can for her," she said, "but she don't speak no English. Only Spanish, and she won't learn nothin' else. Well, I'm too old to learn Spanish. I guess we'll just go on makin' signs. She don't eat nothin' hardly. And cry, cry, cry, from morn till night. Where all those tears come from beats me."

Another time when Japhet's lawyer, Jacob Squires called to arrange about some household money to be paid at Japhet's orders, Doña Mercedes refused to see him; she sent word by Huldy that she was ill.

"Is she ill, Huldy?" asked the lawyer.

"No, of course she ain't. I look after her good. She's just walking back and forth, back and forth, in the long hall upstairs, cryin' and cryin'. That's what she does all day, every day, mostly. She stands by the windows just cryin'. I believe she's watchin' for a ship to come to take her home. She makes signs to me that looks like it. And she keeps a satchel packed all the time, right handy."

But the rescue ship to take the miserable Doña Mercedes back to her family in Tortuga never came. A tiny black-clad figure, she continued to prowl the glass prison, looking ever out to sea, weeping and wringing her hands. A tall tortoise-shell comb stood straight up from her coiled black hair, in the Andalusian style, and on it was draped a long black lace mantilla.

One day, Huldy complained of terrible pains in her stomach. She went home and stayed there for three months, unable to do any work. Almost at the same time this happened, Japhet returned from one of his protracted voyages to the China Sea. When Huldy's sister offered to come and help out, he said "No use. I'm off again any day now, and I've decided to take my wife with me. I'll take her to visit her family." Some time later, on a dark, sleety night, Japhet sailed away.

Two years later, he returned to the Front Street house, without Doña Mercedes. When he was asked where and how his wife was he said, "She hated it here. Couldn't speak English. Had no friends. I persuaded her to make a good long visit to her family. I'll bring her back next voyage."

But Captain Wedderburn did not come back from his next voyage. While the Black Arrow was rounding Cape Hatteras, outward bound, Japhet Wedderburn died of a heart attack.

The big white house was sold to a son of Jacob Squires. Soon after his family moved in, his daughter, returned that day from boarding school, said to her mother at dinner, "Have we acquired a Spanish governess for Tommy and Beth, or who is the woman I saw in the upstairs hall as I went up to change?"

Her mother looked puzzled. "A woman? Spanish? In the upstairs hall? I don't know what you are talking about."

"I do, Mamma," Tommy, aged twelve, spoke. "I've seen her, too. Just at dusk she appears. She's awfully little. She wears a funny thing on her head and a long veil. She seems sad. I thought she was crying."

Succeeding tenants of the Wedderburn house down the years have seen a tiny, childlike woman in dingy black. She wears a tall comb in her hair and a long black lace veil. Usually she walks before the observer, as if trying to show him something. She will stand in front of one of the big windows looking out over the sea. Crying, wringing her hands, and pointing desperately, the woman stands a few moments, then turns and dissolves into the shadows.

In 1925, the Wedderburn house was sold to a charitable organization that proposed to make the house into a summer-vacation retreat for underprivileged children from the cities. Repairs were in progress. A large hearthstone in front of the fireplace in the library was cracked and chipped. It was decided to remove the fireplace entirely and tear out the partition. When the workmen pried up the stone, a wooden coffin was found in a hole that had been dug under the hearthstone. So small was the coffin it was thought at first that the female skeleton found in it was that of a child. The back of the skull rested upon a magnificent tortoise-shell comb of Spanish design. In fragments of dust and decay, ragged as a cobweb, the strands of a black lace mantilla partially swathed the skeleton.

Stones of Fear

BELFAST, MAINE

BARBARA HOUNDSWORTH was born in a small cottage in a village in Cambridge Farms, now Lexington—about ten miles from Boston. A tall, thin girl, she had a plain, sallow face and a halt in her speech. People did not want Barbara in their houses, as a maid or in any other capacity. While she was not in any way deformed or monstrous, her looks repelled them. Life for her was lean and sear. She was the only child of a man who did odd jobs around town. Her mother, a bigoted, unfriendly woman, died when the girl was sixteen, and her father, hoping to better himself in Boston, simply set out, with no thought of saying so much as goodbye to Barbara.

So she went to live with Dame Weller, an old crone of German descent, who eked out a meager living by collecting herbs and simples and brewing berry cordials, which she sold to the villagers. One of her popular remedies was dried nettles, pounded into a powder and mixed with bear's grease, which was guaranteed to relieve aches and pains of the joints. Dame Weller taught the sallow, silent Barbara what herbs to gather, how to pulverize and blanch, how to mix the proper ingredients in cordials and unguents. But in the year 1650 the dabbler in simples had to be very wary. Superstition was rampant. Witchcraft, a bogy with many heads, was a terrible accusation, punishable by death—the agonizing death of burning at the stake. Stoning by crazily hysterical mobs of farmers and villagers often preceded the burning. And a woman who was quick with healing was often accused of witchcraft, willy-nilly.

One day, when Barbara was in her fortieth year, old Dame Weller was

136

found dead, lying at the doorway of her cottage. Froth stained her lips, bubbling whitely long after death. A man who had come to the door to buy a flask of dandelion cordial for his wife found the woman. That night, talk in the taverns and in shuttered cottages bordering the village green was of witchcraft. Could she have met death through her familiar, Barbara Houndsworth?

The next day, when Barbara was out in the fields searching for herbs, two of the village vestrymen searched the Weller cottage. No sign was found of a pet crow, a frog, a lizard, or even a cat. Such were used in witchcraft. For a while, Barbara was left in peace.

Then misfortune struck. The small son of one of the vestrymen fell out of a tree, cracking his skull. The child died, foaming at the mouth. A dull murmur of fear crept through the branches of the trees and along the eaves of Cambridge Farms.

The third calamity, which was to seal Barbara's fate in the village, was the simultaneous discovery of a pet squirrel in her cottage and the decline of the beautiful daughter of the leading church elder. The girl took to her bed on her wedding eve, screaming that she could feel tiny teeth gnawing at her vitals. This was too much. The elder and a group of men proceeded to Barbara's cottage. Breaking in the door, they found the woman hiding in the cold fireplace. At her breast she clutched a terror-stricken squirrel, which she had found in the woods and brought home as a pet.

"Her familiar!" roared the elder. "Her familiar is killing my daughter, ripping at her vitals."

Barbara was seized and dragged off, loudly wailing, to the village jail. There within two days she was, after a farcical trial, pronounced guilty of witchcraft.

The morning she was awakened to be led to the stake was a dreary day; fog drifted across the village green in dank swathes. The jailer went out to talk with a carter who was to act as lighter of the fagots.

By some good fortune, the door, which was neither latched nor locked, swung back. Slowly the woman, dressed in a sackcloth shift, rose to her feet, listening. No sound. Like a fragment of the fog, she slipped out of the door and, in an instant, was lost in the mist.

Loud was the outcry when Barbara's disappearance was discovered. The villagers were more convinced than ever that the woman was an archfiend. How else could she escape through tightly bolted doors? For, of course, the jailer, when berated by the elders, stoutly held to his story that he had barred the door from the outside when he left. A witch of darkest dye was this woman.

Keeping to the woods and byways, traveling only at night, stealing fruits and vegetables from orchards and gardens, and slaking her thirst from brooks and springs, Barbara came after many weeks to a village called Belfast, in Maine. Here she found a small, half-derelict cottage near the rocks bordering a small inlet, a tiny bay from which one could row easily out to sea. At first, the woman thought to ship to some port in southern waters. Some island, perhaps in the West Indies. But as time passed, she gave up the idea.

Because Barbara knew no other way of life, she started in again as a compounder of simples and cordials. For a time, she prospered. Her aromatic remedies seemed to find favor. Her cures were remarked. She lived quietly away from people and was left strictly alone.

Then the Furies struck again. A short way from Barbara's cottage lived a drunken woman with a son whom she beat severely on almost no provocation. The boy, Lanny, one day went to Barbara for consolation and, finding a friend in her, visited there more and more often. Often he accompanied her into the woods and fields to hunt herbs. Sometimes they would row out into the bay to gather kelp and mermaids' hair, a silky seaweed containing iron. Meanwhile, the mother of the boy objected to his friendship with Barbara, "that old hag who grunts like an animal."

One day, Lanny's mother was bedded with colic. Holding her belly with both hands, she staggered out of bed and into the village, shouting that she was bewitched and she knew who had done it.

At first, the people of Belfast refused to believe the half-demented accuser. But other odd things occurred. Cats and dogs ran riot with rabies and distemper. Cows and swine died of a peculiar black pestilence.

Then at midnight, with no wind blowing, no living soul about, the church steeple burst into flame. The meetinghouse was entirely destroyed.

Next morning, men were sent to manacle the woman, Barbara, and bring her to the courthouse. As she was being led across the green, Lanny's mother rushed toward the shackled woman and hurled a stone at her. The crowd following instantly roused to demoniac sadism, and even the kindest villagers scuffled for stones to hurl at the defenseless woman. Cries of "Burn the hag!" rang out.

One who flung stones more frenzied than the rest lifted a rock in his two hands high above his head. Hurling with all his might, he sent the stone wide of its mark, and it struck the forehead of the town clerk, who held one end of Barbara's shackle. The man uttered a piercing cry and fell, bleeding, to the roadway. In the pandemonium that followed, Barbara broke away from her captors and, swift as lightning, ran into the woods that bordered one side of the green.

Straight for the rocky path along the sea the woman fled. She could hear cries and shouted commands behind her. The woods was thick; fear and the slenderest streak of hope lent wings to her feet. In spite of her heavy manacles, she soon outwitted her pursuers, for the woodland paths were many and devious, and she knew every foot of the way—every turn, every hollow and rise of ground—from days spent foraging.

After a while, the sun was clouded over. A wind and gusts of obscuring rain aided the woman's escape. When she reached the rocky path to the headland, she knew there was a chance for freedom. But the rocks were wet, slippery, and the woman was fast tiring. Her feet were cut and bleeding. The thin shift donned for her burning dragged in tatters about her thin body. Panting, almost spent, she took one more step upward. Her ankle doubled under her, and with a moan she fell backward into the sea.

A thin, wild-haired woman, hands manacled in front of her, is seen by walkers inland and by fishermen from the bay, wandering on the highest point of the rocks. Reports that she has been seen usually presage a storm at sea. Many times, survivors from wrecks off this treacherous coast have seen the woman regarding them somberly as they scrabble up the rocks. As they reach safety, she disappears.

Summer visitors to Belfast and the villages along the stretch of coast from Rockland to Searsport tell of seeing this apparition wandering amid flocks of sea gulls. The cries of the gulls, which the ancient Greeks call the lost souls of drowned sailors, mingle with cries of the anguished woman—Barbara Houndsworth, tried and condemned to burn as a witch.

Crimson Footprints

NEW LONDON, CONNECTICUT

SOMETIMES one sees in a museum or in a private collection of memorabilia of a past age aquatints, pen-and-ink drawings, paintings on glass, or crewelwork samplers of landscapes peopled with figures. Usually it is the charm of costume that holds the eye. In such case was I drawn to a set of eight small aquatints, framed in curly maple (much in vogue in the seventeenth and eighteenth centuries), placed as a frieze under the mantel shelf in a house in Connecticut. When I asked the owner about the figure—a young girl in blue cloak and bonnet—that appeared as the central motif in each picture, she smiled.

"All I know is that the girl is a kind of legendary figure hereabouts," she said. "I bought the pictures at an auction where the lares and penates of an ancient New England family were being sold. The girl in question, Lottie ap Enken, was "witched away" from a tavern sometime during the early seventeen-hundreds. She was a member of the Elihu Yale family, I believe. Now she haunts the woods and seashore near the old tavern. I'll tell you as much as I know about her, if you like."

Here is the story.

Elihu ap Enken started as bound boy on the Yale farm, near Litchfield. He was industrious, well liked, and studious. In short, a boy who would, everyone said, go far in life. When he was eighteen years, he pocketed his meager savings, plus a present from his employer, and set out for New London, where he proposed to hire out to a taverner.

There is the place to make money these days, thought young Elihu, as he plodded along toward the seacoast. Coaches running back and forth all day long. Lots of travelers. A man hears the news of what goes on in the world. I'll be a tavern keeper. That's the life for me.

At first, Elihu washed the pewter pots and plates in the scullery of an ordinary of not too good repute near Norwich. After a brawl between drunken marketeers, in which two men were killed and the place made a shambles, the boy lit out for New London.

Within five years, Elihu had his own tavern—the Wild Goose, named so because he was partial to the dark-fleshed game and always had good luck when he was out shooting in the marshes. He was a talkative man, friendly and welcoming. Elihu heard all the news of the world, as he wished, and prospered mightily. He became a leading citizen in the village of New London.

One night, a woman, cloaked and veiled, arrived on the Willimantic-Saybrook coach. It was a cold night. She was carrying a baby, heavily swaddled against the night air. A room, the best in the house, was given over to the woman, for by her clothes and manner she looked as if she were used to the best. Dinner was served in her room. Soon afterward, she retired. It being a cold, blowy night in December, not many convivial spirits were abroad. About eleven o'clock, Elihu doused the candles and locked the iron-studded door. By midnight, the Wild Goose showed dark and quiet.

Between midnight and dawn, a woman dressed in cloak and veil slipped out of a side door of the tavern. Glancing up and down the roadway, she hastily followed a path branching off into the woods. A few minutes later, the sharp metallic ring of iron-shod hoofs penetrated the still night; then the sound diminished to silence.

As dawn was cracking the gray sky over the marshes, Elihu was awakened by the sound of wailing. Sitting up in bed, he tried to collect his thoughts. That was a baby crying. Of course, the only baby in the tavern was in the best chamber. "Well," he grunted, scratching his head, "I hope she nurses the child, or whatever they do to quiet them. It's waking up the whole house."

But the crying continued. When Elihu and one of the kitchenmaids knocked at the door of the chamber, there was no answer. The woman had gone. On the bed, still swaddled, lay a tiny baby girl. Pinned to the outer blanket, which wrapped the baby as would a cocoon, was a note:

"Dear, kind Elihu,

You did not recognize me. I am Emma Yale. You did not know it when you were bound boy at the farm, but we are cousins. Now in my wretched state I leave my daughter to your care. Be kind to her and provide. I am going to England.

Emma"

Lottie ap Enken, as the girl was called, grew up to be the angel of the neighborhood. She was a sunny-tempered slim slip of a girl, with round blue eyes and masses of tawny ringlets.

From the time she could walk, Lottie wore bright-red shoes and a voluminous cloak of military-blue cloth. Walking along the roads around New London, Lottie could be tabbed a long way off by the tripping red shoes. The girl seemed to dance instead of walk.

Her adoration of big, bearded Elihu was proverbial, as was his for her. He would snatch her up at all times of the day, no matter what age she was, and toss her in the air, saying, "You weigh thistledown, no more. How can you be so light and not blow away? Be careful, for I can't spare you." Then he would kiss Lottie's cheek and put her down.

It seemed to the townsfolk that Lottie was always bound on errands of charity. Basket on arm, she would hunt out the oppressed, the sick—even the shiftless, of whom she would hear no evil—to bring food and medicines. When she was sixteen, all her spare time was taken up with her charitable rounds. Elihu said to her, "You've more halt and blind and yawpin'-mouthed beggars at your heels than I can provide for. You'd best call a stop somewhere."

One day, Lottie heard of a poor woman, old and sick, who lived in a deserted farmhouse, half tumbled down, far out on the Saybrook turnpike. Carrying medicine and food, the girl walked all of an afternoon to find the place. When she did, for the first time in her generous life she felt afraid. The old crone was a dreadful sight. "A face like a wart hog," as Elihu said later. Her hair hung in dirty, stringy eldritch locks, and through her broken teeth the creature uttered whines, protesting that her dying hour was near. It was rum she wanted, not food or medicine.

Once Lottie had left the bleak house far behind, she resolved never to go near the woman again. But the old horror had made a resolve, too. She would see the girl again. She would have all the rum she wanted.

From that day on, the woman hung around the Wild Goose. At first, she whined and begged at the kitchen door or at the half door of the taproom. To shunt her off, the tap boys would give her the dregs left in the mugs of other people. Then, one morning, Old Dreary, as the boys called her, waylaid Lottie, who was just starting on her rounds. Shrieking and moaning, the woman complained of raging pains in her bowels. She wailed that she had been poisoned by the tap boys. To quiet the woman, Lottie gave her some rum, bidding her never come near the place again, on pain of being handed to the watch. Elihu came up at this time. He added more warnings. "If I ever catch you around here again, ye old wart hog, I'll shoot the heart clean out of yer carcass!"

Crouching away into the woods, the old crone made signs with her claw-like fingers and spat like a cat. Two or three times after this episode at twilight or later in the evening, Lottie thought she saw the face of Old Dreary half hidden behind trunks of trees in the woods behind the tavern.

Lottie decided, soon afterward, to go to a spelling bee, which was to be held in the evening, at Mistress Danby's house, half a mile down the road. She dressed carefully—a white challis gown, her crimson shoes, the circular blue cloak, and a wide gray beaver hat tied under her chin by red ribbons. As she came downstairs, Elihu spied her. Catching the girl in his arms, he tossed her into the air as he had done ever since she was a swaddled baby.

"Oh, Father, put me down," Lottie protested.

He said, "Spell them all down tonight, Lottie, for the honor of the Wild Goose. You've never looked so pretty."

Lottie bowed to the men sitting around the long table near the fire and went out the tavern door. She was never again seen alive.

A wide search was instituted directly the girl's absence was discovered. There was no snow on the iron-hard ground, and no footsteps, Lottie's or another's, gave any clue to which way she had gone. Mistress Danby said Lottie had never turned up at her house. Elihu ap Enken, brokenhearted, continued the search for months.

Half a year passed. Two or three times, kitchenmaids or tap boys told Elihu they thought they had seen Lottie, in her blue cape, hovering around the back door of the tavern. Each said that, when hailed, the figure faded into the woods.

Elihu, candle in hand, went up, one night, to his bedroom. Force of habit took him to the window, where he stood staring at some drifts of snow blowing in waves across the yard. He straightened. Was that a flash of red? It looked like dancing feet clad in crimson shoes running to and fro. Racing downstairs, the man searched among the drifts. The chalk-white snow was crisscrossed by footprints red as the berries on a holly tree.

A few days after the midnight dance of crimson footprints, two hunters, looking for shelter from a snow squall, stumbled on a brush-clogged cave near Saybrook; they dug in to wait out the storm. To their horror, the half-decomposed body of a young girl lay twisted on the floor of the cave. Both men knew the blue cloak, the red shoes, and the beaver hat with red tie ribbons. Everyone within a radius of fifty miles had loved the girl who wore them. Searching the cave, the men found a dirty, ragged old shawl and dried scraps of food. Too, they found that the arms of the girl had both been broken.

No clear solution was ever put forward of just how Lottie was lured away from her destination on the night of the spelling bee. Old ones nodded heads wisely. One crooned, "Aye, aye, witched away she was. By Old Dreary. She was a witch out of Endor. Always said that." Another nodded. "Dorcas and Margy Abbott were witched away like Lottie when I was a girl. Lottie was witched away surely, for threatenin'. Threatenin' Old Dreary."

Always in winter, when snow lies whitely on the ground, the dancing ghost of Lottie ap Enken is seen flitting hither and yon. Afterward, footprints, red as blood, are traced in the snow.

The Drifting Dory

CAPE COD, MASSACHUSETTS

SINGULARLY illusive are the ghostly apparitions that haunt the seaways. There are many tales to bear this out—the Flying Dutchman, the Bridal Barge of Aran Roe, the story of Grace Darling, the English lighthouse heroine, at her eternal rescues in raging storms. For two centuries, sailors have told of seeing the mist-blue barkentine La Belle Hélène burning to the waterline. These and others are little more than mirage, will-o'-the-wisp, or perhaps flickering phosphorus fires. Coupling the sight with legend, the imagination quickens and builds. Ghostly appearances are, in any case, what we make them.

Just so are the constantly reported appearances, off the coast of Massachusetts, of a sharp-prowed dory. Drifting in the sea lanes, the dory causes captains of tramp steamers, pleasure yachts, even transatlantic liners to reduce speed and attempt rescue. Both by day and night the dory is sighted. No captain's rescue crew has yet succeeded in reaching it.

One of the first recorded instances when the drifting dory was seen is in 1880, when a small coastal steamer, the Nantucket, plying between New York and Boston, stopped to effect a rescue. The record was made by a passenger on the steamer.

A raging sea, caused by winds of almost hurricane volume, had swept the seacoast from Jacksonville to Mount Desert Island for three days. Damage to waterfront houses had been extensive. It was high summer, and many craft had been at sea. The wreckage that littered the bays and beaches would enrich beachcombers for months.

The night, as so often happens after a destructive storm, was soft, with a light land breeze and an almost placid sea. A passenger on the Nantucket walked on deck, enjoying the hour when Sirius, the Dog Star, brightest planet in the firmament, descends to sleep with the sun. Twilight was just deepening when, a few miles from Provincetown, he heard a distinct "Hallo-o-o, hallo-o-o, to starboard!" Thinking it was a lookout, the man scanned the masthead with his binoculars. No lookout was to be seen.

It was then he discerned a black boat of the kind fishermen use for short-distance trawling. The craft, which was drifting on the light swell, lay about two hundred yards to starboard. Leveling his glasses, the man could see that the dory was exceedingly battered. In the bottom of the boat was the body, horribly mutilated, of a white man. Standing in the bow, unsteadily, as if in great pain or fatigue, was a gigantic Negro in bloodstained rags.

Quickly the man summoned a sailor, who sought the captain on the bridge. Up to now, no one but the man with the glasses had either heard the cry for help or sighted the dory. Speed was reduced to a crawl and a boat lowered. Six sailors rowed about for half an hour, but not the faintest trace of the dory or its bleeding occupants was found.

When the spectral dory is sighted at night, a kind of phosphorescent aura seems to hover around the craft. Always there is heard the "Halloo-o-o!" If the boat hailed in this manner gets close enough to the dory before it disappears, seemingly into the waves, the bloody figures of the white man and the Negro can be plainly seen. The dory also drifts closer inshore; people in trawlers, small sailing boats, and rowboats have reported seeing it.

One holiday party tells how startled and horrified they were to sail round from a bathing cove near Martha's Vineyard and almost ram the dory. The women shrieked while the men affected a calm they did not feel as the dory drifted past, disappearing in a light evening mist. The members of this party vouchsafed that as each gazed at the spectacle of the black dory and its grisly passengers—one dead, the other dying—there drifted across the water the stench of rotting flesh, mixed oddly with the pungent odor of spices.

The Moaning Oak

VIE FORTUNE PLANTATION, HAHNVILLE, LOUISIANA, 1865

ANY PERSON compelled to be abroad on the open roads in the relentless November storm that had tortured the bayou country of Louisiana for five days would be fortunate to come through alive. Winds of hurricane velocity had turned the bayous into raging inland seas, and the Mississippi had burst its levee at two points, flooding the surrounding plantations. Thousands of live oaks had been uprooted or sundered by the lashing wind, and now lay tangled in sodden mattresses of Spanish moss, like recumbent prehistoric animals. Once-proud avenues of oaks leading from the bayou or levee roads to galleried houses had lost half their complement of trees. When this storm, the most terrifying within anyone's memory, abated, the accumulated destruction of property would be gigantic.

About midnight, of the fifth day, the wind died perceptibly, and one could hear the writhing and soughing of the oaks in the woods to the east of the Gailbraith plantation, Vie Fortune.

This wide, thick belt of trees—sycamores, pecan, black walnut, and poplar, with here and there a massive old white oak—lay between Vie Fortune and the slave cabins, which ran in a straight line for a quarter of a mile toward the bayou. At one end of the woods stood a big sugar warehouse, and at the end near the bayou, a little removed from the other cabins, was the log-and-brick three-room cabin of Mammy Effen Garry.

Mammy Effen—so called for her frequent admonitions, beginning "Effen yo don' git"—was a privileged character at Vie Fortune, for her long life of varied service on the plantation was fully appreciated by the Gailbraiths. She was very old, and her days of work were over. No one rightly knew—least of all she— exactly how old she was.

Somewhere around 1790, Alexander Gailbraith had purchased six Gullahs, black as obsidians, straight off a slave ship that had put into Pointe a la Hache, in the Gulf. One of them, a quiet, magnificently built girl of about twenty years, had been trained as a house servant. In her deep musical voice, she had told Emeline Gailbraith, mistress of Vie Fortune, her name. It sounded more like "Garry" than anything else, so Garry she had become.

In the beginning, she was a sort of second nurse to the three small Gailbraith children. All adored her, and it was not long before she ruled the nursery. Later, she became cook, and then, for the past few years, a sort of housekeeper-*cum*-confidante to Miss Sally, the spinster mistress of Vie Fortune. There had been no male Gailbraith since the War Between the States; three Gailbraiths, father and two sons, had given their lives to the Confederate cause.

Tonight, as the storm was blowing itself out, Mammy Effen, in a collection of old cloaks and shawls, sat huddled over a fire of walnut husks and wood chunks in the one room of her cabin that she used. The other two were storage rooms for apples, potatoes, and sacks of hominy grits and meal.

Mammy Effen was crooning to herself. "Trials and tribulations Lord, you done work yo'sef up pow'ful high dis time. Trials and tribulations— What dat?" She straightened in her hickory rocker, listening intently. "Sho' nuf, dat am a chile' cryin'." Now that the wind had died to almost nothing, the sound of a human being in distress was plainly audible. She walked quickly over to the split-log door, lowered the night latch, and swung the door wide. There, sprawled in a crumpled heap almost across the threshold, was a young girl. The old woman saw at a glance that the girl was unconscious and blue with cold.

Old as she was, Mammy Effen had extraordinary strength when the occasion warranted. Stooping, she gathered the frail girl in her arms. Then she pushed the door behind her and laid her burden on a pile of fur skins Miss Sally had sent to be made into a rug.

All through the night, the woman worked over the girl. It seemed she would never regain consciousness. Hot mustard-water rub. Hot barley and milk gruel forced through the tightly clamped lips. Finally, when dawn was a slit of yellow in the gray east, the girl breathed easier; a shade of color stained her cheeks, and she slept as would a child.

For three weeks, Mammy Effen tended the girl. She emptied a room of provisions and made in it a soft bed of the fur skins, which she covered with a fine linen sheet—a present from the big house that she had never used. The days were still mild, and a wool cloak sufficed as covering for the girl.

In all this time, the girl never spoke and seldom opened her eyes. That she was gaining strength with good food and care, Mammy Effen knew. Her color was good and she breathed freely now—no longer the awful rattle in the windpipe she had suffered through the first few days. Not many of the slaves ever came to Mammy Effen's cabin. They had their work to do, and since she was much older than any of the others, she did little socializing. There was small chance that anyone would know the girl was there until such time as the old woman wanted it known.

One thing puzzled Mammy Effen. She wondered if the girl herself knew that she was with child—a little over two months, she calculated. There were no mysteries about pregnancy in Mammy Effen's book. One of her proudest boasts was that, in her early years when she had been sent to the stud cabin, she had conceived immediately. In seven births she had borne her master six lusty male children.

Now Mammy Effen sat and watched. Outside, she heard Big Nate and Boro and Lige and her grandson Corffy, whose eyes were so crossed he ran in two directions, clearing away the debris. A few cabin neighbors came to her door to report how hard the storm had hit other plantations, but she did not ask any of them to come in. "I's a destruction ob dat sto'm, I is," she told them, shaking her turbaned head. "I caught a misery in ma back. Jes' yo let me sleep." So they let her sleep.

One bright morning, the girl lay sleeping in a shaft of sunlight. Mammy Effen, whose eyes were not sharp any more, drew her rocker close to the bed and peered at the girl's face. The old woman saw a delicately bred young woman, small in stature and light in bone, a finely chiseled face, with a pointed chin, a wide brow, and a generous width between the eyes, and golden-brown hair as soft as spun silk. Mammy Effen sighed and uttered one word, "Quality." The girl opened her eyes, and for the first time she smiled. Then she took the big, strong, wrinkled hand of the slave and stroked it. "Thank you," she said. "Thank you always. When do you think I might get up?"

Mammy Effen stood in the door of her cabin, looking toward the big house of Vie Fortune. She was mightily worried. "Scarified, dat's wha' I is," she said to herself. "Caise I don' know what to do. Cain't get a word out'en her. Mo' tribulations Lord, yo's ridin' me mos' to death." She folded her arms across her chest and rocked back and forth woefully.

Turning back into the cabin, the woman approached the girl, who was sitting in the rocker close to an open window. A light breeze stirred the crisp curtains and lifted the waves of the girl's hair.

Mammy Effen said, "Now chile, we gotta settle dis. Yo been in ma cabin nigh a month. Nobody know ya here, caise I don' teln 'em. I ask ya who yo is, wha ya come f'om. Yo on'y smile and won' speak. Dat ain' right, nohow. Effen yo don' teln me what I ask, I gotta go to Miss Sally."

Looking up, her eyes blank of expression, the girl answered, in a dull voice, "I'm nobody. Where I come from doesn't matter. When I'm able to walk without being so tired, I'll go on my way. You have been so kind to me. Be kind and humor me. Go to Miss Gailbraith, if you wish. It doesn't matter."

"But what about yo folks? Dey's prob'ly cryin'—crazy dis minute wid worry. Why yo don' lak dem?"

The girl said, "Because they don't like me. If they're worried, it is only because I disobeyed them. They—my father and my brothers—wanted me to marry a rich old man so they could live on his money. That's all I can tell you."

Mammy Effen marched up the branch-littered avenue of Vie Fortune in midafternoon. She pushed open the front door of the house that she had served for over seventy years and mounted the gracefully curved staircase, with its polished mahogany treads and handrail. She knocked lightly at a double door at the front of the second-story gallery.

"Come in. Oh, Garry, it is you. I am happy to see that you suffered no hurt in that terrible blow. I was about to send Hannibal down to see why you had not come to visit me. Come here. Sit beside me." Miss Sally Gailbraith motioned to a hassock near the *lit de repos* on which she rested.

"Dat sto'm upset my calc'lations about visitin' yo ev'y week lak yo tole me, but beside dat I got a misery in ma mind. Ma mind's all tore up wid woe." Mammy Effen settled herself on the hassock. Miss Sally smiled her lovely smile, which was quite in accord with everything else about her. So many miseries had she listened to—and, she hoped, solved—for Garry, once her adored nurse and always her cherished friend.

"Tell me, Garry. Let me help."

"I know'd yo'd help. But it ain't for myse'f. It's for a young lady. Quality lady, and for a lil' baby wa's comin' one ob dese days."

In the lengthening shadows of the afternoon, Mammy Effen told the mistress of Vie Fortune the story—how she had taken in a sick girl, nursed her to health, and now was faced with the problem of the next step. What was she to do?

"You will do no more, Garry. You have already done too much. I will take on from here. Send her to me tomorrow. Hannibal will take a buckboard to fetch her."

The advent of a girl without a name caused scarcely a ripple of interest in the household at Vie Fortune. Except for three house servants—Hannibal, who was butler, general factotum, and eldest son of Garry; Miranda, a housemaid; and ponderous old Juna, the cook—Miss Sally lived alone. Every once in a while, some kin or other would pay her a visit of varying duration, so the servants accepted the girl as a mysterious relation. Miranda advised Corffy, who ran errands for Miss Sally, that he "better shet his mouf, pesterin' to know who was de young miss. When da time come, we know."

One day, Miss Sally came into a room where the girl sat, listless as usual, with a book of engravings on her lap. "Now, we have got to have a name for you. I insist," she said, her usual gentleness pointed with determination.

For a long while, the girl looked out the window, then she sighed. "You can call me Josephine."

Miss Sally waited. "What is your other name? Your true name."

Again the girl waited, watching the swaying garlands of Spanish moss eternally twisting in the wind. Then she shuddered. "Darrell," she said. "Josephine Darrell."

Miss Sally rose from her chair in surprise. She walked over to the fireplace. With her back to the girl, sitting so still in the deep-cushioned chair, she said, "Josephine Darrell. Then you come from Olantho Plantation, near Natchitoches. Your father is Boone Darrell."

Many weeks later, Miss Sally Gailbraith sat in her writing room composing a letter to a distant cousin, Paul Delaunoy, who lived in the vicinity of Natchitoches. If anyone could give her Josephine Darrell's story, it would be Paul. As unofficial historian of the bayou families, he knew what made the skeletons in their walnut armoires rattle ominously from time to time. Short of going directly to the dissolute father and brothers of Josephine—truly a last resort—it was Paul she must question.

Miss Sally had asked Josephine, during a conversation, if she knew Paul Delaunoy. Josephine said she did not, so Miss Sally had decided to ask him to Vie Fortune for a short visit. In her letter she admonished her cousin to gather all possible news about the notorious Olantho Plantation and what was known of Josephine Darrell's flight.

Just after lunch on the day Paul Delaunoy was expected at Vie Fortune, Miss Gailbraith suggested to Josephine that she should walk through the woods to Mammy Effen's cabin and take her a jar of sage apples. Wrapping a pale-blue wool cape tightly around her figure, which plainly showed that she was approaching her time, the girl, in her usual listless manner, swung the small basket of conserve on her arm and set off.

An hour or so later, Mammy Effen got up from her chair to fetch a stone she used for cracking walnuts. As she passed the window, she chanced to look out. Under the wide-sweeping branches of a magnificent old white oak tree across the dooryard from the cabin stood Josephine Darrell. She was gazing up into the branches, one of which swept almost to her feet in a gnarled arc. Then, at the top of her lungs, the distracted girl shouted, "I won't! I won't! I'll never bear his child! I hate him too much!" Mammy Effen strode across the dooryard toward her, and the girl dropped the basket and ran into the woods.

Paul Delaunoy was nothing if not thorough when unearthing family scandals and the misfortunes that so relentlessly pursue some families. The story he told his Cousin Sally behind the closed door of her writing room was this:

Olantho Plantation had been inherited by Boone Darrell, the eldest son of Pollux Darrell, a rich planter of indigo, and, later, sugar. Boone was called back from Paris to take over the plantation, and he arrived with a mistress from Martinique, whom he palmed off for years as his wedded wife. At that time, the plantation was as splendid as any in Louisiana. After a few years, he tired of his mistress and packed her back to Martinique. He then married a widow from Natchez, who was so wild in her ways that she terrified any visitors who came to Olantho. However, she bore Boone Darrell three sons and a daughter. After the last childbirth, her mind cracked; the mother of Josephine and the three Darrell boys became a raving lunatic. For a while, she was confined in one of the larger slave cabins. Then, one night, the massive black woman who was her bodyguard was found drunk on the floor of the cabin. No trace of Boone Darrell's wife could be found. Two days later, her body, clad only in a cheap wrapper, was fished out of the bayou below Cypress.

From then on, during the years that Josephine was growing up, life at Olantho became a three-ring circus. No more devious or profligate men infested the gambling clubs and bordellos of New Orleans than Boone Darrell and his sons. The plantation fell into near ruin. Every possible way of raising ready cash was explored.

Finally, Boone Darrell happened to notice that his young daughter Josephine was a handsome, fresh, and highly desirable girl. Immediately he set about to find a buyer. His murky eyes rested on a man named Eberhard, an old planter from one of the early Dutch families who acquired huge sugar acres in the vicinity of New Orleans in the early seventeen-hundreds. This aging Lothario had buried three wives and was ready for a fourth. Somehow—probably from a slave—Josephine, then in her eighteenth year, got wind of what was afoot. She waited until her father and brothers were again in New Orleans on one of their periodical razzles. Then she gathered together a few belongings and fled the locality. For a time, the father made some attempt to locate his daughter, but with no success. Now the four Darrell men were living like poor white trash at Olantho, with the sheriff expected any day.

When Miss Sally and Paul Delaunoy came out of the writing room, Josephine was sitting on a chair in the hall. She still wore the blue cloak, pinned tightly at the throat, that she had donned for her walk to Mammy Effen's cabin. Her face was streaked and dirty from her wanderings in the woods. When Miss Sally introduced Paul, Josephine nodded dully, seeming scarcely to see him. Almost as if she were walking in her sleep, she went wearily up to her room.

A few hours later, Miss Sally took a tray of hot food to the girl's room and found her, fully dressed, sitting beside the window, staring out across the woods. Suddenly she turned. "Miss Gailbraith, I must tell you something. I ran away from our plantation. I went to marry, as I thought, a young man who had been a schoolteacher in the village near us. He was moved to a school at Plaquemine.

I *had* to run away—I cannot tell you why. When I found him, I discovered he had a wife already. He had deceived me. This is his child I am carrying. But I hate him. I will not bear his child."

Miss Sally took the distraught girl in her arms. She spoke soothingly to her and said that all would be well. She would look after her. Early in the morning they would make plans.

It was a still, cold night along the bayou. A moon bright as crystal hung high. Mammy Effen couldn't fathom why she was so restless. What was wrong with the night? Something. That was mighty sure. "Tribulations. Nothin' but. Why ma mind so rickety tonight?" Was that a creaking of branches? There was no wind to rustle the old white oak tonight. The woman moved over to the window, pulled back the curtain, and looked out into the brightness. Then her heart seemed to stop. With a gasp, she flung open the door and dashed out to the foot of the white oak tree. A few feet from the ground dangled the body of Josephine Darrell; the blue cloak—silvery now in the cold moonlight—pinned tightly around her throat was held tighter by a rope slung over a branch that arched almost to the ground. A short ladder, lying on its side under the body, shone like a piece of burnished metal in the brilliant moonlight.

Mammy Effen cut the cold, lifeless body down and carried it all the way to Vie Fortune, there kicking at the front door until Paul Delaunoy and Hannibal came to let her in. Miss Sally came hurriedly downstairs, and the sobbing old Gullah woman laid the dead girl on a couch, then sank to her knees at Miss Sally's feet.

Mammy Effen was as independent an individual as ever stepped, and she loved looking after her own ease in a fine warm cabin, yet a few weeks after she found the stiff body of Josephine Darrell hanging from the white oak, the old woman asked her mistress to be allowed to come back to Vie Fortune to live. She confided to Miss Sally that she could not stand the moaning and crying that came every night at the same time, from the branches of the oak. Near midnight, which was the hour when she had caught sight of the silvery-blue cloak of the suicide, the moaning commenced. For an hour or so, it continued. And was not just the moaning of a grief-stricken soul. It was the deeper, more agonized moaning of a woman in labor.

Down the years, the oak tree has become a kind of symbol to stay away from. Those forced to use the bayou road at Vie Fortune—no longer in the Gailbraith family—either do their business in the daytime or give the tree a wide berth at night.

Known in the locality, indeed far afield in the state, for its grim associations, the moaning oak has more stories to its credit than any other tree I can recall. No storm or wind is needed for it to writhe its branches in anguish. On still nights of summer, when a puff of air is a rarity, the venerable old white oak can put on a wonderful show. Some persons say that on brilliant moonlight nights, if one looks closely, a swaying form in a pale-blue cloak may be seen among the branches.

A Frosty Evening
for the Figure Eight

CENTRAL PARK, MANHATTAN, 1880

GEORGE ADE once wrote a sparkling article on the bizarre characters he encountered in the streets of New York. He remarked that he was constantly seeing "sister acts"—real or make-believe—fabulous to behold. Sometimes—not always—these women were, like twins, dressed alike. Usually they resembled each other to a marked degree.

Seldom were they young; generally they were spinsters of uncertain age. Graying, dressed in shabby finery or just shabbily, painted or withered, smiling gaily or aristocratically aloof, inebriated or sober, scavenging or palpably affluent, the weird sisters of Manhattan Island haunted the city streets. What, Ade wondered, were the stories behind these eccentric humans.

Most of the stories we will never know. Now and again, one or both of a sister act are found dead in some junk-littered room in a mean street or a fashionable quarter. The story is pieced together by rapacious newspaper reporters and comes to light. "Incredible," we say, over our morning coffee. But nothing involving the extraordinary idiosyncrasies of the human brain is incredible.

One story I was told, about a pair of Manhattan sisters—real ones, this time—came from an old New Yorker who knew them well.

The fine brownstone mansion built by Norden Van der Voort on Fourteenth Street just off Fifth Avenue in 1850 fired the admiration, and often the envy, of

157

everyone who passed its heavily corniced façade. Van der Voort was of old New Amsterdam lineage, a wealthy banker, and married to beautiful, imperious Netje Schermerhorn. What more could a man ask?

Norden Van der Voort did ask more. He wanted an heir, desperately. But Netje always fenced. "Wait, Nord. I must have time. You're too set in your ways. My social activities will not allow me to confine myself. Not yet."

A few years passed. Then Fate took an interest and a firm hand. Netje gave birth to a daughter. In two years' time, she gave birth to another. The double blows to Van der Voort's pride were augmented almost beyond bearing by the doctor's verdict that Mrs. Van der Voort could never have another child. The thwarted father of two unwanted daughters sailed for Europe, alone. In three years, he returned, but not to live in the Fourteenth Street house in amity with his family; he hied himself to a summer place he owned near Rhinebeck. There he shut himself away from friends and family. It was rumored that he drove fast horses and entertained even faster women from Albany.

Meanwhile, life in the New York house continued on a relatively even keel. The elder daughter Netje had named Janet. In a romantic mood, she named the second girl for a Roman friend of her girlhood, Rosetta. Janet and Rosetta Van der Voort grew up in a sheltered atmosphere, with occasional summers spent in Europe. Only rarely did they see their father. Their mother and father, as the gossips put it, were "living apart."

When the girls were fourteen and sixteen, Norden Van der Voort was killed; a team of fast pacers bolted, wrapping a cut-under, with Norden in it, around the trunk of a huge elm tree on his estate. Mrs. Van der Voort promptly sold the Rhinebeck house. She did not like the air of debauchery, real or fancied, that hovered over it.

Janet and Rosetta were never apart. If they had been twins, the two girls could not have been closer. Their particular stamping ground was Central Park. This tract of land in the heart of the city of their birth was to them what the cave of jewels and delight was to Aladdin.

"We are New Yorkers through and through," Janet often remarked.

"Oh, my, yes, we are," Rosetta chimed in, giggling.

From the time the girls were of an age to be presented to New York society, they were a problem to the fastidious Netje Van der Voort. Neither of her daughters cared the least iota for masculine attention. Neither even wanted to learn to dance. Skate, yes. That they loved, because the ice rink in Central Park was such fun, and, too, they could skate together. Nobody else was needed.

One day, Netje took a good long look at her girls. Janet was full-bosomed and well-thighed. Her hair was dark brown and inclined to be crinkly. Her eyes were her best features—large and luminous brown. "Yes," Netje said. "She will do with proper dresses to set her off."

Rosetta was much smaller in build than her sister, plump, pink and white, and jolly. A bit of a tomboy, her mother suspected. Her hair was red—not carroty, thank heaven, but red. It curled charmingly and her hazel eyes snapped in fun. She giggled inanely. Too bad. But then, thought Netje, the boys will find her a far more diverting companion than Janet.

So couturiers were called in for advice. In a few weeks, both girls were presented to society. First, there was a lunch party at Delmonico's, at Broadway and Twenty-sixth Street; the decorations—American-beauty roses and wreathed smilax—were the last word. The next night, a ball was held in the spacious reception rooms of the Van der Voort house. This was a triumph; the music, the food and wine, the favors, from Paris, for the cotillion—all were superb. But the young men remained aloof, seemingly almost wary of the sisters Van der Voort, for the extremely legitimate reason that neither of the girls cared a tinker's damn for the young men.

Netje couldn't understand it, though she didn't honestly care. Truth to tell, she was flirting with the idea of marrying again. Carl Whitridge, a famous sportsman and beau, was pressing for her hand. Now that she had launched the girls, she proposed to enjoy herself. Could she help it if they were duds socially?

So Janet and Rosetta spent hours every day in Central Park. Always beautifully dressed in the height of prevailing mode, both Van der Voort girls were veritable fashion plates.

Winter was the season of unalloyed bliss for the girls. They went skating on the rink in the morning, then to lunch at Delmonico's or Louis Sherry's—sometimes, rather daring, in the Palm Court of the Holland House—then back, in a hansom or victoria, to Central Park and skating all afternoon.

Of course, some days had to be given for fittings. Special frocks, with bustles, not too large but brilliant enough to catch the eye, were worn for skating. One never appeared after lunch in the toilette one had worn in the morning.

Both Janet and Rosetta became so proficient in cutting every kind of figure on the ice that they were tagged by names: the Figure-Eight Girls, Miss Ice Age —for Janet, who was haughty—Melting Icicle—for Rosetta, who seemed always on the verge of letting some man skate her around. Sister Janet scotched that. "Better not start," she said. "One never knows where familiarity will end."

When the girls were in their late twenties, their mother succumbed to the proposals of Carl Whitridge and married him; the newlyweds sailed for Europe directly after the wedding. The girls never saw their mother again. In two years, Whitridge died. Shortly after that Netje cabled her daughters that she was to become Comtesse de la Farge-Pontet. She expected them to come over for the wedding. But this was winter, Janet replied; they simply could not leave the winter carnivals and skating tournaments.

So obsessed with skating did the girls become that springtime, summer and autumn eventually held no charms for them. In fact, their inactivity during the other seasons irritated them until they quarreled with each other in sheer exasperation. During those months, deaf to the invitations of their mother to visit her at Chateau Ferrier, in the Auvergne, the sisters shut themselves up in the New York house, or, when the humid summers got too much for them, retired to a secluded cottage near Cape May. Here they saw no one and seldom made any of the excursions for which the locality is famous.

Then the Comtesse de la Farge-Pontet died, in her chateau; Janet and Rosetta did not go over for the funeral. When their mother's will was read, the girls were surprised, and not pleasantly. The fortune of Norden Van der Voort, which had for a long time withstood severe inroads, was now nearly exhausted. Their lawyers told Janet and Rosetta that with strict economy they could continue to live in the town house; the cottage would have to be sold.

Mr. Sanderson, lawyer for the estate, was emphatic. "You must listen seriously to me. I mean it when I say strict economy. Otherwise you won't even have this house left."

That night, the Van der Voort sisters, who had always gratified every whim that entered their heads, sat in glum silence before a dying fire. Finally Janet broke the silence. "I will carry on with my birthday carnival, just as planned," she said. "The costumes and the favors are ordered. So are the food and entertainment. I cannot stop now."

Rosetta, who had begun to weep, said, "Of course. It will be our last fling. Oh, won't it be awful to be poor?"

The birthday ice carnival given by Janet, to all who could stand up on skates, was a sensation. Here were two rather odd but generous sisters, as much a part of the Central Park scene as the trees or the Zoo, giving a carnival as big as a three-ring circus, inviting anybody who wanted to attend.

"Ye gods," remarked a fellow dressed as a Roman centurion, "this blow-out must have cost a healthy fortune. And given by a pair of gals that won't let a fellow near them. Kinda funny, if you ask me."

The night of the carnival was clear and not too cold, with a high-riding moon. The air was as invigorating as champagne. Colored lights and fireworks gave a fairy-tale atmosphere to the scene. At one end of the rink, long trestle tables had been laid. Fires in iron basket braziers warmed anyone who needed warming. Waiters on skates served food and drinks. The music was provided by a brass band from Van Alstein's Beer Garden.

The highlights of the evening were the magnificent costumes of the hostesses. It was Janet's birthday, her thirty-fifth, but, of course, what was hers belonged to Rosetta as well.

Janet was costumed as Queen of the Night. She wore a petticoat of rich blue satin, looped with a tremendous bustle of dark-purple velvet; a bodice, cut with peplum and long sleeves, edged with ermine; and a silver bonnet, crowned with a panache of blue and purple ostrich feathers. Not for warmth—Janet scorned such weakness—but because the costumer said it set her off, her hands were thrust into a barrel muff of ermine on which had been pinned a diamond crescent moon.

Rosetta, not quite so dazzling, was Rosetta the Rose. She wore a looped and bustled skirt of green satin garlanded with big pink roses, and over that a coat, cutaway in front, of American-beauty velvet, edged in gray squirrel with powdered mica sprinkled on it like snowflakes. A bonnet of rose-red satin wreathed with roses completed her costume. Indeed, the two rig-outs worn by the Misses Van der Voort were described in the newspapers to the envy of all readers.

When Lawyer Sanderson read the account in the newspaper of his clients' birthday celebration he nearly had a stroke. Janet had purposely not told him about it. In short order, he was closeted with the girls, laying down rigid rules by which they must live henceforth.

The years passed. The Van der Voort house was shuttered and seldom showed signs of activity. No more did the aging spinster sisters go to Central Park. Occasionally, for a few years, they were seen to occupy seats on a Hudson River pleasure steamer. A few times, they were seen strolling on Fifth Avenue in the evening. Always richly, though unfashionably, dressed, talking rather primly together, the two seemed oblivious of passersby.

Until a few years before the sisters died, an old German servant did for them. Finally, she gave notice, and Miss Janet accepted it. The woman told the policeman on the beat, "They're so close with money. They won't feed themselves at all. I would have starved. All day long the two play cards."

In Miss Janet's sixty-fifth year, she died. Relatives from Rhinebeck took charge. Rosetta, Janet's alternate breath, lay prostrate in a perpetually darkened room, and three months later she, too, died. When their doctor was asked what illness took her off, he replied, "An illness not in the casebooks, as such, but more common than we think. A broken heart."

The friend who gave me the details of this story said that during World War I, her son, who was about to go overseas, one night attended a party on Fifth Avenue. When the party was over, he started to walk home, but the brilliant winter night beckoned him into the Park. As he approached the Fifty-ninth Street lake, he was startled but completely fascinated to see two women skating, hand in hand. One was in rose red, the other in purple. Both sported huge bustles. Round and round they skimmed, performing figure eights, concentric circles, all manner of fancy twists and twirls. By jove, he thought, here are two professional performers! Suddenly the two women skated close to the edge where he stood. The one in rose red waved and smiled, nodding her head with its coronet of roses. The other woman scowled at him, jerking the arm of her companion. Her lips moved as if she were chastising with cruel words. In a moment, the two were away across the lake. The man waited but they did not return.

The war years passed, and my friend's son returned to New York. A few nights after his arrival, he found himself near the Fifty-ninth Street lake again. It was officially winter, but the lake was not frozen enough for skaters; only a thin film of ice covered the water. He looked at his watch. It was half-past eleven. The young man strolled to the lake edge. Suddenly he stiffened. There were the skating women. Round and round they went, silver skates scarcely touching the thin rim of ice, in figure eights and all the intricate gyrations. With such ease, too! Rose Red and Purple, he called them. On they sped, disappearing into the night.

Go to Central Park some winter night of moon and stars. You will see Janet and Rosetta, too. Many persons have.

Hussar's Gold and
the Woman of Silence

COVINGTON, KENTUCKY, 1890

THIS IS the story of a great friendship, a heart-warming companionship, between a wonderfully understanding woman and a Thoroughbred horse. The comradeship forged in life continued in death.
Near Covington, Kentucky, in the year 1890, lived Mary Wheeldon, a high-
spirited woman who came from a family of consequence in the state. On both
sides of her family tree, the men had held important positions in public life:
senators, a governor, judges and diplomats to foreign courts—all of them with
the added luster of being notable sportsmen. Mrs. Wheeldon carried her head
high; she was a renowned beauty, and her popularity in every class was marked.
In fact, one might have called her a supremely fortunate woman. Most of all, it
pleased Mary Wheeldon that she was the wife of Judge Wheeldon and the
mother of his son.

That she was, as well, a famed horsewoman she took for granted; the
daughter of Randolph Corbett could hardly have been anything else. Her breeding farm, Corbett Acres, which she ran successfully, was known the length and
breadth of the land. On every major race course in the country, her horses carried the crossbar silks of primrose yellow and black to win the coveted classics.
Her knowledge of equine lore raised this delightful woman to a high place in
the hierarchy of the Thoroughbred-breeding world.

For perhaps twenty years after her marriage, good fortune prevailed. Her son Randolph took high honors at the University of Virginia, scholastically and in sports. He shared his mother's fondness for, if not her deep knowledge of, horses. The one crack in the armor of Randolph Wheeldon was that he could easily be led. He seemed fatally addicted to hero worship.

There came a day, toward the end of his senior year, when Randolph, distraught, appeared unexpectedly at Corbett Acres. His mother, who was surprised and distressed at his frantic demeanor, calmed him, and Randolph told her what had happened.

Hero worship had played him false. An athletic coach, whom he had admired, had sold him a bill of goods about a great sports center for which the coach was raising money. This center was to rise triumphantly in Washington. There was even to be a racecourse as part of the attraction. Randolph had signed a note for a large amount of money on a Louisville bank. Now he had heard that the promoter, after collecting money from him and other sources, had hared off to Europe.

Staggering as this news was, Mary Wheeldon told her son not to despair; she would handle it. She did, but it was only the beginning of a series of other adventures into shady finance that seemed to attract Randolph as a flame attracts a moth. To keep these transgressions from her husband was difficult, but she managed somehow.

Then, with no warning, came the deluge. In one month, disaster followed disaster in the family of Judge Wheeldon. First, Randolph committed suicide, in his club at the university. Money again. His last note to his mother was brief: "I am scuttled. Forgive me. Ran."

Hard on the tragedy, a financial crash reduced the family fortunes to nothing. This so deeply affected Judge Wheeldon that he succumbed to heart failure. The sudden, relentless accumulation of horror seemed to unhinge Mary Wheeldon's mind, and she disappeared from the world that knew her.

For years, nothing was heard of Mrs. Wheeldon. For a while, the rumor ran rife that she had done away with herself in some remote place. Her close friends chose to believe that she was living under an assumed identity abroad. After a time, Corbett Acres was sold, and in a world of swiftly moving events the Wheeldon tragedy was nearly forgotten.

Mary Wheeldon had neither killed herself nor gone abroad. She was living in the depths of a sparsely settled locality only thirty miles from Covington. She had never gone farther afield. There, hidden in an embryo forest of saplings she farmed a small property that no one had ever known she had. She lived completely alone, save for one companion—a beautiful Kentucky Thoroughbred stallion.

Later on, Mrs. Wheeldon told the few inquiring visitors who penetrated her seclusion that when she decided to retire, almost immediately after her world collapsed, there had been no one to accompany her but her favorite horse, a two-year-old Thoroughbred named Hussar's Gold. His breeding was impeccable. She had been more than usually fastidious in choosing the mare to breed to his sire, Cavalry March. She had chosen Bright Gold, a superb chestnut mare who carried the blood of the immortal Selene in her veins. No one could conceive of a more delightful companion in solitude than Hussar's Gold.

The stallion had never felt a bridle in his life, nor tack of any description. His manners were as perfect as his conformation. Since colthood, this gleaming stallion had been reared to be a companion, to follow his friend about wherever she went. In many ways, big and handsome as the horse appeared, he filled the place of a watchful bodyguard.

After about twelve years of an almost hermitlike existence, Mrs. Wheeldon, picking wild blackberries one day, came upon two men who had lost their way. After directing them to Lexington, she and her companion, the big golden horse, disappeared into the woods. When the men arrived in Lexington, they lost no time in telling and retelling a story that caused wonder and speculation.

According to their report, they had been taking a short cut but came to a dead end in a tangle of brush. Suddenly there appeared a tall, handsome, but haggard woman in faded calico and a sunbonnet. When they asked to be directed to the highway to Lexington, the woman had answered pleasantly and in a cultured voice. Beside the woman walked a gold-colored stallion. As she conversed, she stroked the animal, a stunning Thoroughbred if ever they had seen one. "They were two Thoroughbreds," ventured one of the men.

The news spread through Lexington, and a man who had known Mrs. Wheeldon in the early days sought her out. No, she would not sell her horse. Yes, she was quite aware that the finest blood in Kentucky breeding coursed his veins. No, and no again, to all who tried to buy Hussar's Gold.

After a time, when various old friends had tried, and failed, to induce Mrs.

Wheeldon to come back to Covington, they stopped visiting her. That was the way she wanted it.

Many times in the following years, people encountered the woman in calico, matching stride for stride the big, well-mannered stallion beside her as the two friends walked across the fields and through the woods near her farm. These two, who had so well found peace in the backlands of Kentucky, grew old together. Tall and straight they remained until the last.

Children, and adults as well, tell stories of meeting a woman in calico in the berry-bush country north of Covington. Beside her, the sun shining on his golden hide, walks a big stallion. Those who claim to have seen the pair say that they materialize suddenly out of the shadows of the pine and scrub oak scattered through the berry patches. Across a sunlit clearing they move. The woman appears to be talking to the horse; he nods his head in understanding. Passing from sight as quickly as they come, the two shades merge again into the dappled sun and shadow of the woodland. It would seem that the two have a long journey ahead.

The Phantom Lighthouse

CAPE HENLOPEN, DELAWARE BAY, 1655

IN THE realm of supernatural phenomena, a building often appears as the spectral symbol. Dwelling houses, churches, and castles—all have figured in ghostly tales. A curious example I came across in my research is that of the old stone lighthouse on Delaware Bay which has never existed to any man's knowledge, but which has brought destruction to ships for three hundred years.

To the shipload of storm-battered voyagers aboard the leaking packet Devonshireman, from Plymouth bound for Philadelphia, the sight of a light to starboard seemed as heaven-sent on that dark Christmas night of 1655 as the star of Bethlehem to the three Wise Men. So many weary weeks had passed at sea that the crowded passengers aboard had lost count. No screeching sea bird, not even a branch of leaves floating on the swell, allowed the least hope that there was any land left in the world. Now a light—a stationary light, not a ship's lantern—glowed brightly through the night, which blew in gusts across a pale, faraway moon.

Captain Faulkner, skipper of the Devonshireman, set his hand to the wheel. This, he thought, must be Landing Cape Light, on the New Jersey coast. Unless a mariner sailed close to the shore here, his vessel would soon pile up on the treacherous submerged rocks. The Captain had made a dozen voyages in the past ten years, carrying Puritan families, followers of William Penn, to Philadelphia. He knew the dangers of pear-shaped Delaware Bay as well as the palm of his hand. On a dark night, it was best to heed carefully the warning light of Landing Cape.

Suddenly a heavy surf seemed to rise all around the rocking ship, a grinding of rocks on wooden planking rent the air, and in half an hour only a few crates and rope-tangled spars marked the spot where the Devonshireman, with two hundred souls on board, had gone down. There were few survivors. Two sailors, cut and bleeding, managed to crawl to a small farmhouse near the shore. They learned that no lighthouse had ever stood where the light had shown. The spot they described was the manorial grant of Henlopen, a mound of turf-topped rock that had once been the site for the marriage festivals of the Delaware Indians.

As the years passed, numerous wrecks were reported at this same blunted headland abutting into the narrow entrance to Delaware Bay. Survivors always described a squat, round drum of rough-laid stone rising out of the drifting mist or rain. In this "tower" appeared a light, not bright and steady like the warning lamp of a lighthouse but composed of fitful flashes, now burning brightly, now dulling down, like an Indian signal fire. Its peril can well be realized, for during rough weather a light of this description can so attract a mariner that he throws caution to the winds and seeks safety where he suddenly believes it to be.

A legend grew, recalled and embellished in the taverns of Dover and Rehoboth. In the early days when the Delaware Indians roamed their tribal lands, the high acres of ground topping the headland, later called Cape Henlopen, were kept sacred for yearly ceremonies. Just as Seven-Hundred-Acre Island, off the Maine coast near Dark Harbor, was used as a betrothal and marriage mound (the island abounds in gigantic, grass-grown piles of clam and oyster shells from betrothal feasts), so this headland on Delaware Bay was put to the same use.

One day, when the daughter of a powerful chieftain was being honored at a marriage festival, a raiding party of British soldiers from a nearby fort surprised the celebrants, killing the chief of the tribe and the young braves. The Indian maidens were carried off, and for days after this outrage their defiled bodies were found scattered in the ditches and on the beaches of Delaware Bay, from Rehoboth to Laurel. The chief's son, brother of the betrothed maiden, escaped the massacre, and fled into the forest. His revenge on the white man, the country people said, was the appearance of the light in the fatal drum of stones.

In 1800, a gaily decorated barge, bearing the family and friends of a Laurel tobacco planter named Barstead, set out for a water picnic. His daughter Louisa

Barstead was to marry one of the Maryland Starr family within a fortnight. Three of the Starr brothers owned houses of delightful name—Faith, Hope, and Charity; Hope still stands.

For this sailing party, all the ladies wore their pastel-colored muslins. Louisa, loveliest of all, was dressed in pink. As the barge, so happily laden, rounded Cape Henlopen from the direction of Rehoboth, the passengers were startled to see the figure of a lone Indian, in a dark blanket and a crest of eagle feathers, silhouetted against the sky.

The Indian, standing immobile, almost like part of the rock, suddenly threw back his head and emitted a loud cry of anguish. Immediately afterward, a tremendous wind sprang up. The sun shone brightly and no rain fell, but waves of tempest proportion crashed the pleasure barge and its terrified passengers against the rocks below the headland where the avenging Delaware stood. Only a few members of the picnic party were saved. Among those who lost their lives was Louisa Barstead.

In 1910, two young men of the region set out on a canoeing trip. It was midsummer; Delaware Bay glittered smooth as a ballroom floor. As night approached, the canoeists rounded Cape Henlopen. Deciding to strike camp for the night, the boys beached their craft and prepared to sleep on the point of headland. Darkness fell; a full moon rose. The travelers were tired from a long day of paddling and soon turned in.

About midnight, one of the boys was awakened by an unearthly, blood-chilling scream. It rose in waves of anguish, then ceased suddenly in a choking sound. Turning to speak to his companion, the boy discovered he was alone. Spurred by terror, he ran toward the place where the sound came from, then froze in his tracks at sight of a dark blanketed shape, standing motionless, seeming to gaze straight through him with burning eyes. The figure motioned toward the edge of the cliff and faded into the night shadows.

The boy searched until morning for his companion. It was only with the rising of the sun that he found him, at the foot of the cliff, his skull split in twain, as if from the blow of a tomahawk.

Mariners claim that the phantom lighthouse still appears. The point itself, Cape Henlopen, is haunted by numerous ghosts, for many unfortunate humans have been victims, down the centuries, of the curse of the Delaware Indian brave.

One poignant ghost is that of unhappy Louisa Barstead, who met death so violently the day of her water picnic. A small slender figure in pink dress and ruffled bonnet, she walks along the cliff edge, searching, always searching. For what? Her lover, young Starr, in all probability. He escaped from the wreckage and married a Maryland girl. Still Louisa searches, wringing her hands and sobbing.

Whispering Floor Boards

NEWBURYPORT, MASSACHUSETTS, 1701

MANY-FACETED is the performance of supernatural visitations. Some rather singular visitations have been performed by ghosts who could go, at will, to a part of the world that had never known their presence in life. Sir Arthur Conan Doyle often referred to them as "journeying ghosts."

In this story, the journeying ghost is La Belle Stuart, the toasted Duchess of Richmond and Lennox, as brilliant a star as ever shone at the Court of Charles II. The world learned of her travels years after the death of Jeremy Probart, the Newburyport schoolmaster whom she visited. A small oval portrait and a silver-mounted velvet jewel casket containing letters were found secreted behind the wainscoting in the room he occupied. This room, in the house of Mistress Deborah Caswell, was occupied by the schoolmaster from the time he arrived in Newburyport from Scotland, in 1701, until his death.

The articles discovered in the schoolmaster's room identify La Belle Stuart as the woman whose ghost often appeared there during his life. The portrait, painted on wood, is of a lovely woman of opulent charms; it bears an astonishing resemblance to the portrait of the Duchess by Sir Peter Lely. The picture is unframed; a leather thong is run through a gold hasp at the top, as if the possessor had worn it on a chain at some time.

The letters are of a woman to her lover, letters bearing a cipher stamped

175

into the orange-red wafer of sealing wax that fastens each of the four fold parchments. The cipher is entwined with the letters "L.L."; thus did Charles II's adored Stuart sign herself to intimates. It stood for "Lennox love."

To my mind, the most significant article is the velvet jewel casket itself. Latticed in filigree-silver *repoussé* roses and thistles, the casket might well be part of the *repoussé* toilet set that, contained in a large walnut box, was presented to Stuart by Charles II. This extraordinarily handsome silver set, long preserved at the castle of Lennoxlove, has recently been acquired by the National Gallery of Edinburgh.

About 1672, when La Belle Stuart was at the height of her beauty, she lent her "person in perpetuity," as she writes in a letter, as model for the figure of Britannia on a copper halfpenny. A coin of this mold is stuck by sealing wax to a corner of one of the letters.

The story of the "Lennox love" cipher, besides being a romantic annotation on the margin of this tale of Jeremy Probart, has much charm of its own. It appears that among the lovers enjoyed by the ravishing Stuart during her richly colored life, none so pleased her, so completely won her heart, as her cousin Lord Blantyre. This childhood sweetheart—"fair and bonny in his form and ways," as she wrote in a journal—was her constant companion for years.

When Lord Blantyre fell out of grace with the King, the Duchess of Richmond and Lennox bought the castle of Lethington, in East Lothian, from Lord Dysart to house her disconsolate cousin. Although it is said to have taken all her savings to make the purchase, it was "a labour of greatest pleasure for dear Trassie." In 1704, the young laird received the title deeds of the castle, with a message, "Lennox love to Blantyre." Ever since that day, the turreted ivy-hung castle has borne the romantic name of Lennoxlove.

Events on this side of the Atlantic began on a stormy September afternoon in 1701. In spite of the bitter wind blowing in from the sea, the long wharf at Newburyport was crowded with townspeople, for the largest British ship to enter that port in many a day was coming in. Captain Wendover, of the stout Atlantic packet Aurora Borealis, out of Bristol, had had no intention of bothering with such an out-of-the-way seaport. But adverse winds and monumental seas had driven the vessel far off her course, until finally the Captain, in vile humor, shouted commands to furl and haul the cast ropes at Newburyport. Slowly now, the high-pooped ship came alongside the wharf.

One of the passengers who disembarked was a tall, rather stoop-shouldered young man in dark smallclothes and a hooded cloak of rough Highland wool. As he held the brim of his dark-colored beaver against the gale, the cloak swirled about a figure so lean it approached emaciation. Viewed closely, the face of this individual, with its high-bridged aristocratic nose and its narrow sparkling brown eyes, proved most winning in expression. It was, furthermore, a keen, intellectual face, the face of a student.

Suddenly a woman's voice called from the gangway, "Oh, Master Probart, shall we be obliged by your company in Boston? When do you arrive?"

The man addressed turned slowly. In the soft, burred speech of the Scottish Highlands, he answered, "Greit an' fair a'd like to. But a'm ain stopping in Newburyport the noo."

The woman waved goodbye and was helped into a chaise by her husband. So came the Scottish schoolmaster to Newburyport.

A few months before this incident, one of the leading bankers of the town, a Mr. Dalrymple, had made a voyage to London and Bristol on business. While there, he conceived the idea of coaching up to Scotland. His forebears had come from Edinburgh to settle in Boston, and somewhere near the Firth of Forth stood the castle where his father was born. Mr. Dalrymple stopped at Haddington, and then dined with the Dean of Galloway College. After listening attentively to stories of the colonies told by his guest, the Dean made a request.

"My good Dalrymple, would it be possible for you to find a post in one of your board schools in Boston, or in your town of Newburyport, for a young Scots student—in a way, a kind of ward of mine? We will call him—er—Jeremy Probart. I cannot—am constrained, in fact—to divulge the details of this laudable young man's background. Let me assure you he is at no fault himself. But all elements concerning his birth touch exalted personages. The Stuart cause is unstable, as you well know. I believe it a wise plan to get this young man out of Scotland, clear away, in fact, to the New World. I can vouch for Jeremy. He is studious and steady, his intelligence is of a high order. His parentage, alone, precludes his taking his rightful place in the world—a matter of inheritance and the bar sinister. You understand?"

Before taking leave of his host that night, Mr. Dalrymple had promised to find a place for Jeremy Probart in the board school in Newburyport whenever he should arrive in Massachusetts.

Excellent lodgings had been prepared for the new schoolmaster at the house of a widow of means, Mistress Deborah Caswell, a cousin of Mr. Dalrymple. The house, which stood in the middle of a garden, enclosed within a white picket fence, was a short way out of town on the Gloucester turnpike. In the ordinary way, Mistress Caswell did not take lodgers. But to accommodate her cousin Dalrymple, who seemed determined that the young Scot must have the best lodgings in town, she had fixed the big parlor on the second floor for the young man's use. "And a vastly handsome chamber it is," she told a neighbor. "I hung a taffety tester on the bed in the alcove and put my best hand-woven rugs on the floor."

From the first sight Jeremy had of his lodgings, he was genuinely pleased. Except for the times when he had stayed with Great-Aunt Gordon-Lennox at Ayr and slept in a grand four-poster in a tapestry-hung chamber, he had never dwelt in such luxury. Most of his life—ever since he could remember—he had been shunted from one foster parent to another. When he was small, he had lived on farms or in village houses. Then he went to school, many schools, in different parts of Scotland. The last few years he had spent at Galloway College.

Only once had something exciting interrupted the comparative somberness of Jeremy's childhood. It had occurred on a rare visit to Great-Aunt Gordon-Lennox. One evening, he was sitting in a broad window seat in the gallery with a volume of poems by Sir Richard Maitland. He was reading the poem wherein Maitland sings the praises of Lethington Castle, and had just come to the lines

Thy tower and fortres lairg and lang
Thy neighbours does excell;

when a commotion broke forth in the withdrawing room. The doors were flung wide, and before Jeremy knew what was happening, he was swept into the arms of a richly dressed woman he couldn't remember ever having seen before. She smelled of roses, and the great plumes of her hat nearly smothered him as they dangled over his face. Finally, he slipped from her arms to sit, spellbound, on a hassock at her feet, scarcely able to answer the lady's questions for awe. Her appearance, strange and dreamlike, reminded him of the damsels in Spenser's "Faerie Queene."

Jeremy noticed that this beautiful woman who made so much of him looked warningly several times at Great-Aunt Gordon-Lennox and at two gentlemen who accompanied her. Was some secret abroad? A servant, bringing wine and fruit, called her "Your Grace." Later, when Jeremy was in bed, supposedly asleep, the lady tiptoed in and kissed him, whispering, "My bairn, so bonnie, so like Trassie." In the morning, she was gone, nor could he ever find out who she was.

The years in Newburyport passed uneventfully for Jeremy Probart. Quietly popular with students and townspeople, he found happiness in his work and in such diversions as walking in the meadows, an occasional coach journey to Boston or Rockport, the spelling bees and simple games he organized. To fill his evenings, he accepted a few tutoring students. Thus life sped past the Scotsman, scarcely touching him with its wake.

One night, Jeremy sat later than usual over the composition of a narrative poem he was working on to read at the end-of-term exercises. The story, a great favorite of his, he had heard in childhood from his Great-Aunt Gordon-Lennox. Jeremy was often asked by his students to tell the stirring tales of Scottish lairds and the conflicts that had for centuries kept the border of Scotland around Carlisle a conflagration of hates and jealousies.

His quill scratched on: "In 1651, the Earl (later Duke) of Lauderdale gave to a woman of his tenantry a massive silver chain known locally as Midside Maggie's Girdle. The Hardie family held Tollis Hill, a farm on the Lauderdale estate bordering Midside. Thomas Hardie was so much from home that the farm was managed by his strapping wife, Margaret Mylestone, known throughout the valley as Midside Maggie.

"After a terrible winter, Hardie found he had lost so many sheep in blizzard drifts he was unable to pay his rent.

"Maggie stood before the Laird and told him their plight. The Earl beetled at the woman. 'If there is such a wealth of snow on Tollis Hill, I'll forgive ye the half-year rent if ye can bring me a snowball in June.'

Nothing daunted, Midside Maggie found snow in the dells, the season hanging late. She took a snowball to the castle. The old Earl was as good as his word. He remitted the rent. Maggie prospered, putting the farm on a firm footing. Shortly after this, the Earl, who stood staunchly Royalist, was taken prisoner at

Worcester, while his lands were forfeit. For nine years, he lay a chained captive in English prisons. The Hardies saved their rent, term after term. One day, Maggie, having collected it all in gold pieces, baked them in a bannock. She then set off on foot to London to offer it to her imprisoned Laird.

"The Earl was released at the Restoration. In return for Maggie's devotion, he gave Tollis Hill rent free to her family for the rest of their lives. At the same time, he gave Maggie the silver chain, which for years she wore as a girdle."

Jeremy, completing the poem at last, was about to sign his name and the date when his hand paused, arrested in midair. What was that? A whisper? Who could be whispering at this time of night? A gentle susurrus drifted across the room. From the floor boards rose the sound of a woman's silken skirts sweeping past. The whisper took form. "Footsteps"—"footsteps"—"footsteps." The scarcely audible echo died away.

On an evening soon after this strange occurrence, Mistress Deborah went into Jeremy's room to prepare his bed. Only the fitful light from nearly burned-out logs in the fireplace gleamed upon the walls. The dame was startled to see the figure of a woman in a sweeping satin dress, with jewels and ribbons in her hair, sitting in the low chair beside the hearth. The toe of the woman's slipper rocked gently, to and fro, an ornate cradle, which seemed to be carved and painted, surmounted by a crest with coronet.

As Mistress Deborah stood amazed in the doorway, the figure at the cradle leaned over and smiled at the sleeping baby. Then, rising, with finger to her lips, the woman disappeared into the shadows behind the bed.

When Mistress Deborah rather hesitatingly told her lodger what she had seen, he seemed interested but undisturbed. "I think I know the meaning of these visitations," said Jeremy. "Later, when I am sure, I will tell ye."

Jeremy closeted himself in his room. He removed a loose panel in the wainscoting. From the space behind the panel he extracted a small portrait and a velvet jewel casket. Carrying them to the table, he sat down, looked long at the portrait, and carefully read and reread the five letters sealed with "L.L." He had concealed these articles in the voluminous folds of a tartan shawl of Gordon plaid.

Before he left Scotland, Jeremy had paid a hasty visit to Great-Aunt Gordon-Lennox, an immensely old woman now. She had given him the portrait and the casket containing the letters. In a quavering old voice, Jeremy's Great-Aunt had said, "Ask me no questions, laddie, I'm held to a promise. But keep the picture by you and read the lines carefully. Read *between* the lines. Ye'll ain know yer maither an' yer faither." The greeting of endearment in the letters varied only slightly. "Beloved Trassie,"—"Dearest Trassie," and always the letters were signed "L.L."

Again, of nights, Jeremy heard the sibilant whispers "Footsteps"—coming nearer—"footsteps," and the soft sound of silken movement, as though invisible feet paced up and down the room.

Then, one day, a long-looked-for letter arrived, an answer to one Jeremy had written to the Dean. Yes, the letter said, Her Grace the Duchess of Richmond and Lennox had died over two years ago, died in delirium, fearing that her enemies were tracking her down.

After Jeremy had seen the woman rocking the cradle before his fireplace a number of times, he sought out Mistress Caswell. "I have come to tell ye I know the woman who haunts my chamber. It is my maither. She was called La Belle Stuart. She is dead now. The cradle is empty. It is I she ain rocks, or sai she minds. She feared her enemies. That's why she whispers. Ye'll nay telt a soul, nay?"

One winter night, Jeremy Probert died, quietly, as he had lived his life in Newburyport. It was not until many years later, when workmen were repairing the paneling in the Caswell house, that the velvet casket of letters and the picture were discovered. A son of Mr. Dalrymple took the portrait of La Belle Stuart and the casket of letters to Scotland to repose among Stuart treasures at Lennoxlove.

TRILOGY OF THE FAR WEST

America on the Move

PRAIRIES OF SOUTH DAKOTA, 1943

MANY a traveler by rail in the days when the American Indian was still a majestic figure on the broad prairie entertained listeners with stories of seeing a lone Sioux brave ride as close as he dared to the fearsome iron horse as it smoked and rumbled over the gleaming-hot rails. It happened many times, to many trains. The brave, who wore his war paint in leopard-like spots, rode a big bony type of hard-bitten mustang as black as coal.

The procedure never varied. When the train was on a particularly open stretch of prairie, the painted Sioux brave astride his black horse would take a stand at right angles to the approaching train. Then as the cinder-belching iron monster rolled abreast of the Indian, he would let out a bloodcurdling war whoop, wheel his horse, and, galloping at full strength, race the train. Little by little, as the engineer put on more steam, the train would draw away from the racing Sioux. Never seeming to tire, the mustang ran with unslackened pace. He was just outstripped by greater speed.

Frederick Remington was one of the travelers who saw the indefatigable young Sioux. The artist jotted in the margin of a sketch he made that his hair had stood on end as he watched the magnificent co-ordination of the muscles of the mustang and the rider breasting the wind. Under the sketch he wrote, "America on the Move."

In 1943, a Chicago newspaper reporter wrote a story he had got from a commercial traveler, who, in the course of a year, rode most of the trains in the Western states. The man frequently made the night trip from Minneapolis to Butte.

According to the traveler, he was awakened one night by something he could describe only as "a damned uneasy feeling—as if something was happening that I did not know about but ought to." He occupied a lower berth about midway in the sleeper. There seemed to be no unusual noises—nothing but the steady pounding of the wheels of the coach.

Then he thought to lift the shade of his window. There, so close that he could almost have touched the flying figure, rode an Indian brave, hideously painted in daubs of bright yellow and red. As the man stared, fascinated, at the sight, the brave, who looked neither to right nor left but straight ahead over the ragged black mane of his horse, passed out of his line of vision, as if his great-hearted mount was gaining on the train. The man said that he had seen the identical manifestation five or six times after that, always at night, in different parts of the Dakotas or Wyoming. Always he was awakened from a deep sleep by a feeling of unease.

It would seem that the black mustang, who always lost the race when alive, had gained greater powers in the Valhalla where courageous horses go after death.

Ordeal by Fire

PAWNEE

IN THE sketchbook of the late Frederick Remington, which I once saw in the house of a friend who collects Remington's paintings of American Indians, the stark daring of Pawnee, Sioux, and Apache warriors is vividly evoked. In masterly strokes—for Remington sketched his subjects with quick, sure dashes of charcoal or pencil—he portrayed lithe young braves racing across the page on scarred, scrawny little mustangs. The sheets of paper become the limitless prairies of the Far West, where the pictured savages ride like greased lightning, muscles of pony and rider rippling in exertion. The boys are naked as jay birds except for crudely braided topknots or stubby braids of coarse hair stuck with heron and eagle feathers. Under Remington's fast-moving pencil, all the pure cussedness of mustang and pinto pony comes to life.

In his paintings, in water color or oil, the horses and riders are daubed with red-and-yellow paint. Mean as the little half-wild horses were, the Indian boys loved them above all else. Many of Remington's notes in the margins of his sketchbook tell of their devotion.

One sketch in particular caught my attention, probably more than any other in the sketchbook. In the margin, a long descriptive note had been written telling that Remington drew his sketch after hearing the story I relate here.

It was often the custom among Indian tribes to send a young brave, on reaching puberty, alone into enemy country to test his ability to spy and fend for himself. Little Deer, a young Pawnee, was sent by the chief of his tribe, at Deep River, on such an expedition. Days of crawling through the tall, dry grass of the prairie nearly exhausted both boy and horse; the vast expanse of prairie,

185

farther than the eye could see, rang like brass in the dry heat of a terrible wave of hot wind.

Finally, the time came for Little Deer to return home. On the eve of his journey, there was no hint of breeze as he lay down beside his pony to sleep. The night sky glowed hot and golden with myriad stars. Toward morning, the boy woke to the touch of refreshing wind on his bare back, but with the coolness there was another change, which brought instant fear to the quick senses of the Indian. For he smelled smoke—acrid smoke. Little Deer leaped to his feet, and stood transfixed. Not half a mile away, a great wall of livid flame, crested by billows of black smoke, was racing forward with wind-wave speed.

Springing astride the mustang, already crazed by the glare of onrushing flames, the boy wheeled his mount and struck off for the pale line of foothills near Deep River. The horse lay out in lengthening strides to escape the heat that was now like a furnace behind them. Suddenly the wind slacked and the tall grass grew more sparse, causing the great wall of flame to diminish slightly. As the foundering horse neared a small dry arroyo, his hoof touched loose shale and he fell heavily in the path of the fire.

The young brave was pitched into the arroyo where he lay, dazed, for a few moments. Then, slowly, he got to his feet and saw his horse, stumbling down the bank, horribly burned. The mustang, only just alive, again fell to the ground. Now, if ever, thought Little Deer, looking at his beloved mount, he must prove that he was a true brave. Not only for love of his horse, the strongest emotion he had ever known, but to find favor in the eyes of his chief and his gods, he would save the dying animal. Using every ounce of his strength, he dragged the horse to the muddy remains of a water hole a few yards down the gully. There he dug a pit in the mud and half-submerged his horse. Meanwhile, the fire above them burned itself out.

For days, never thinking of food or rest, he poulticed the animal with cool, slimy mud, mixed with herbs and healing leaves, which the medicine man of his tribe had given him when he set out on his journey. After some time, the horse was able to move. Then his master led him slowly, for the splotched hide was still raw and tender, back to the tribal camp beside Deep River. When, later, Little Deer told his story around the campfire, the chief caused a warrior headband of red beads to be placed on his forehead and a song to be made of his bravery and devotion.

Soon after this, the Pawnees, engaged in a skirmish with United States cavalry. Among the slain Pawnee braves were found the bodies of Little Deer and his flame-seared mustang.

Prospectors and, years later, cowboys often told of having seen a young Pawnee warrior leading a scrawny mustang. Head thrown back, the youth chanted some sort of tribal saga. Some listeners who understood Pawnee dialect said the chant extolled the bravery of a warrior and his love for his horse.

Sometimes the singer remained only a voice, heard in the still watches of a prairie night. Protected by the towering walls of a lonely canyon, a cowboy would turn in his blanket, sit up, and listen. The shrill song of bravery and freedom in the wilds reverberated among the crevasses of the canyon.

Prospector's Pony

COLORADO

THE HOT SANDS astir with tumbleweed and waving sagebrush, the steep battlements of painted canyons, the far-flung panoramas of red rock, the snake-like gray arroyos—all abound with ghosts. Stories are told of lost prospectors who died of hunger and thirst and returned later as ghostly apparitions to haunt the men who had found riches—often the very wealth the victims had sought in vain.

Ghosts of men, horses, lean and hungry hounds are encountered. Sometimes the shade simply wanders down to a water hole and drinks, then ambles off again into nothingness. A horse, a mule, a tiny burro, or a mongrel dog was often a prospector's only companion in the days when so many thousands of gold-blinded men set off alone to dig in the earth and rocky hillsides and pan the streams for hidden riches. Now the ghostly critters toil slowly along, heads hanging in thirst and weariness, seeming almost a mirage in the vibrating waves of heat.

A lonely, utterly weary apparition has been reported haunting the arroyos of Wyoming and Utah for the past hundred years. It is a tiny, pony-size cayuse, which appears only in bright moonlight, casting, of course, no shadow. The pony is laden with bulging saddlebags and a top pack to balance. The top pack appears to be slit open, for in the light of the moon radiations from jewels, apparently of immense value, wink brilliantly, sending forth streams of kaleidoscopic color. Although this richly packed little animal meanders fairly close to campfires and prospectors' huts—or, nowadays, ranch houses—at the first hint of dawn in the eastern sky, he merges with the landscape.

188

Where would a lonely prospector find a horde of jewels? Bandits who robbed stagecoaches and travelers often cached their loot in remote caves in the canyons.

One of my favorite stories concerns a prospector's pony. A trio of cowboys were sent from a ranch near Laramie, in Wyoming, across the Colorado line to bring in a herd of wild horses. On an evening when they were camped beside a stream in a fertile patch surrounded by arid land, one of the cowboys motioned across the stream. "Whose cayuse is that? Hain't seen nobody 'round."

The other boys looked in the direction he pointed. There stood a curious-looking cow pony with what appeared to be a prospector's pack on his back. The pack was a heavy one, roped and hung with cooking utensils and prospecting gear. The animal, which looked half starved, was of a dirty, nondescript gray; pack and horse seemed all one color.

"Don't look real, somehow," one of the boys remarked. The pony stood motionless, watching the boys intently. Then, as if he wanted to tell them something, he tossed his head and walked a few paces away from the riverbank, then turned again, looked at the three watchers, and walked still farther away.

Finally, one of the boys decided to see what it was about. He crossed the stream and followed the pony, who kept always ahead, a hundred yards or so. Branching off, the animal led the way through a cave-like tunnel in a high pile of rocks that guarded one side of the river. Through a low cave they went, where only a hint of light filtered through a crack in the rocks.

And then it seemed that the ghostly pony realized his task was done. Perhaps he was obeying a last whispered instruction from his master, who now lay, a greenish moldering skeleton, on the rocky floor of the cave. One can almost hear the weak voice of the prospector whispering to his pony, "Go tell somebody there's a rich vein of gold here."

The cowboy searched the cave for some clue to the identity of the dead man. Finding nothing, he turned to look for the wraithlike pony, but that wise little cayuse had vanished. Later, men brought from a nearby assayer's office found a rich vein of gold running from the floor of the cave to the river bed.

Madonna of the Uplands

THE OZARKS, ARKANSAS, 1860

She slays and her hands are not bloody,
She moves as a moon on the wane,
White robed, and her raiment is ruddy
Our Lady of Pain.

FROM "DOLORES," BY ALGERNON SWINBURNE

WHEN the Creator swept into color and form the great mountain ranges of the North American continent, the result was wondrous to behold: the Great Smokies, violet-crowned in illusive haze, rusty purple in the deep-hollowed valleys; the Allegheny Mountains, of gray and moss-green crags; the tender romance-hung distances of Virginia's rolling Blue Ridge Mountains; the fabulously painted Rockies; the sleepy, tapestry-colored Cumberlands. For those who seek the very essence of the pioneer stamp of America, there are the gently mounting reaches of bronze-mauve and yellow known as the Ozarks.

The diffident, inarticulate dwellers in this mountain fastness are like a race apart. In a cabin of one big room, or two to three small ones, an entire family—ten to eighteen, usually—lives in almost complete silence except for those occasions when the "boys," as all males in the Ozarks from birth to death are termed, "go swichin'" into the forest to find hidden stills, and the cabin is "red up" by the womenfolk. On the return of the boys, a regular hell and hallelujah of a party takes place, pandemonium reigns for days—at least until the liquor gives out—

191

and then the quiet of the grave descends on the exhausted household. Even small children take part in the liquid banquets. It seems extraordinary that these drinkers of an almost lethal brew, raw moonshine, should reach the stature they do. For the mountaineers of the Ozarks are a powerful, tall, lean, rangy race.

The story I am going to tell is of a gaunt, completely inarticulate woman of the Ozark foothills. She was ugly-faced by most standards, but her body was graceful in its swinging stride, and her enormous cloudy-gray eyes reflected in their depths all that is magnificent in nature, allied with an almost fanatic mother love.

Life for Laurie May Maumsey had been a raw, bitter deal from the time she could remember. First off she was unwanted in the huge, rickety cabin where she was born. The cabin was perched, like a defiant old eagle, on the side of Boston Mountain, the highest spur in the Ozarks. It had been built by Laurie May's grandfather, long before Daniel Boone had come tramping through the mountains with his scouts. Old Deefer Maumsey—called so because his one word of conversation was "Heh?" as he cupped his ear—had envisioned a passel of young 'uns; the Maumsey clan was famously prolific. The cabin, built of pine, had one room and a loft big enough to house a troop of cavalry.

Until Laurie May's mother, Letsy Kilmer, came to live there, the visions of Old Deefer had materialized. Young 'uns seemed to ooze from every crack in the planking. But Letsy Kilmer (Kilmer women never bothered to take the name Maumsey seriously when they took up with Maumsey men) was puny and a bad breeder. She had only six children by Rust Maumsey and his brothers (few Ozark children were ever sired by one man alone), and died giving birth to the girl that got called Laurie May. Soon after Letsy died, Rust went off over the mountain, Jasper way. Last was heard of him, he had taken up with a woman at Eureka Springs.

All Laurie May's brothers were grown up by the time she was eight years old. They were usually off hunting or wenching, so she spent her time wandering in the woods or helping Miz Cutter, at the crossroads general store, with her babies. Babies—human, varmint, or tiny fledglings in the nest—were the very pulse of life to Laurie May.

When she ranged the woods, it took her the entire day, and sometimes far into the evening, to pay visits to all her charges. Down by Zink Run Creek, there were baby otters and muskrats. There were cottontails in the fernbrake and a family of blue tits with a flighty mother in the cottonwood grove. There were chipmunks, and squirrels so small she could hardly find them, in the burned-out hollow stump.

Once, Laurie May found two tiny bear cubs, alone and whimpering. She made a hammock of her ragged homespun apron, put the cubs in, and took them home. But the next day, as she sat on the steps feeding them corn-meal mush, the furious old mother bear came lumbering around the corner of the cabin. Laurie May dropped the cubs and the bowl of mush and legged it into the big room, shutting and barring the door. Just at that moment, one of her brothers, Jake, gun on arm, came up the creek path. He saw the whole thing and shot the mother bear dead. Laurie May did not get the cubs, as she hoped, for after skinning the big bear Jake 'lowed he'd take the cubs over the ridge to Fort Smith. The Army boys would pay high to have the cubs to play with.

When Laurie May was eighteen—a tall broad-faced girl whose roughly hewn features contrasted curiously with her immense gentle eyes—Jake brought home a strange traipsin' woman from over back of the Blue Mountain. It was the first time in three generations a Maumsey had taken up with any woman but a Kilmer. The two clans had practically peopled the Ozarks around Boston Mountain.

Lide, Jake's woman, soon made it plain she "didn't want no smell of that thar big face" around the cabin. So Laurie May went down the long, winding path to the crossroads store to work for Miz Cutter.

For fifteen years, Laurie May Maumsey worked for the Cutters, caring for the children. For fifteen years, the woman longed night and day for her mountain cabin and the long views of wooded hills and valleys—bright and clear-cut at sunrise, shimmery in the heat of noon, softly radiant at twilight. ("Why, Miz Cutter, more colors in that valley than they is in your best block-silk spread," Laurie May once said, in probably the longest sentence she was ever heard to utter).

The silent, shiny nights when the wood doves crooned in the trees, were favorite with the mountain woman. Then wild turkeys honked and scrambled for places in the old sycamore tree, and when finally the moon rose, its rays burnished the feather-sheathed backs of the sleeping gobblers. No princess in a castle tower ever had so magic a picture book as the one that had surrounded Laurie May in her mountain cabin.

When Laurie May was thirty-three years old, she came into the Cutters' store one day, holding their smallest child. "Miz Cutter, Jake just come down from the mountain," she said.

"Yes, Laurie May. What does he want?"

"He says Lide's gone off traipsin'. He's goin' off."

Mrs. Cutter waited, almost reading the girl's mind. "You want to go back to the mountain? To your cabin? Is that it?" she asked.

"I reckon so. Don't feel baid, Miz Cutter."

Laurie May lived alone in the cabin overhanging the valley for about a year. She walked the hills and forest paths as she had done as a growing girl, visiting nests and burrows. All animal life knew her as a friend. She had a little vegetable garden, where she hoed her turnips, pumpkins, and squash in the cool mornings, and, beside it, a small tobacco patch.

One day, a man came up the creek path—a tall, spare man, with crinkly yellow eyes, named Lank Kilmer. He "set himself in" and stayed on. He had a way with him, did Lank, like the other men in his family. Now, after many years, a Kilmer man was sleeping with a Maumsey woman in the big, drafty cabin built by her Grandpap Deefer. In the night, Laurie May, lying awake, guarded in her strong hands the first great happiness she had ever known.

Her child, a boy, was born on a fine February morning; Lank's aunt, Cloe Kilmer, the midwife of the locality, officiated. In the mild days that followed, Laurie May, wrapped in shawls, lay on a hickory bench on the porch, and every few minutes, she took a long and loving look at her son, in a cradle beside her.

Like all Kilmer males, Lank was chancy. However agreeable they had a mind to make themselves when courting, restlessness soon took over. And what restlessness did not accomplish in Lank's case, raw liquor did. It was not long before he was spending more than half his time in saloons in Jasper or Fayetteville, or with old moonshiner cronies who ran stills in the caves of the forests near Blue Mountain.

Now and again, Lank appeared at the cabin, wild drunk, and badgered Laurie May to give him her tobacco money, which she hoarded to buy things for little Lank. When she backed into the shadows of the cabin, silent as a cornered animal, Lank chased her out and beat her across the breast and face. Usually, after these outbursts, Laurie May would find him next morning, lying like one dead, in a drunken sleep somewhere along the hill path.

When little Lank was a year old, his father burst into the cabin one night, raging moonshine drunk. Instead of going over to wrangle with Laurie May, who was busy with a cookpot at the hearth, the drink-crazed man snatched the baby from the floor and turned on his heel. "Now watch me! Whar's that money? If ya don't give me it, I'll bash this brat's head agin the logs!"

For a split second, the gentle gray eyes of Laurie May widened to bursting in her head. A fire of hate seemed to run through her body and dart out of her pupils. She picked up the shotgun that was leaning against the fireplace, and, taking careful aim, shot her man through the throat. As Lank lurched forward and fell, screaming, to the floor, Laurie May dropped the gun and reached for the baby. But she was too late. The child slipped through her outstretched arms and fell, head first, onto the granite hearthstone.

For days after Laurie May had buried Lank, in a shallow grave down by the Beaver Run path, she sat, numbed beyond all feeling, with the body of little Lank across her widespread knees. The weather had come on cold and misty, but the staring woman never noticed. Stark, heavy-eyed—a veritable Pietà—she sat through the long hours, unheedful.

Days passed. Cloe Kilmer hobbled up the path to the high, stilt-propped porch of the cabin.

"Any yo hyer? Whar ya all be?" But there was no one to answer her. Laurie May Maumsey was never again seen in life by anyone.

Many mountaineers tell stories of a tall woman, barefoot, wrapped in home-spun shawls, seen walking hurriedly, with long swinging strides, along a hill ridge. She cradles a baby in the folds of a shawl and is tenderly watching it. The upland meadows know the woman at night and in the heat of summer noon. Usually she is striding. Occasionally, on a moonlight night, this perturbed spirit pauses for a while to gaze out across her valley.

A schoolmaster told me that one night when he was going home from a square dance at the crossroads store, he chanced to look up toward a treeless ridge, an upland pasture. There, like the figure of all maternal grief, stood Laurie May Maumsey. She seemed to gaze first at the moon, then to smile into the eyes of the shawl-wrapped infant. For a matter of minutes, the man stood watching. Then he went on his way. Once, he looked back. The woman stood, silent and at peace, a madonna of the uplands.

Wild-Grape Jelly

LURAY, VIRGINIA, 1864

AMAN walked carefully between the moss-stained trunks of the old
sycamores that lean crazily over the banks of Mary-Ann Creek, near
Luray. This was bad snake country; people hereabouts kept a sharp eye
where they walked. As he looked about him, he saw, deep in the dagger-leaf
bushes, the figure of a long-limbed, slender woman in a faded, berry-stained
dress, a soldier's forage cap on her graying hair and an Army rifle held loosely
in the crook of her arm. If a cottonmouth had reared its head next to the man's
shin, he would hardly have been more startled. It was Miss Hetty Corry—dead
these twenty years—watchful as ever, guarding her wild-grape vines.

A mile or so outside Luray, on the stony Staunton road, old man Corry
drowsed on the porch of his whitewashed brick house. "Odd, sleepy-eyed ole
customer. Don't amount to much, nohow. Jes sets rockin' on the porch, and
sleeps." So Seth Buckley, the harness maker, described Ham Corry to a questioner.

On all counts, the Corrys were a bit of a mystery in Luray and the surrounding villages along the Shenandoah. Everybody knew all, or most things, about
everybody else in the neighborhood. But not about the Corrys. "They keep
shut," people said.

About 1800, a man named Pardue, from Kentucky, a gentleman farmer to
all appearances, had arrived in Newmarket. He cast around for a piece of property. "Not too big a tract," he said at the general store, in his rather high-

197

pitched voice. I aim to build a house and bring my wife from Louisville. She's not robust. I believe the mountain air here will benefit her."

So Winston Pardue built his house over against a belt of woodland on the rise toward Staunton. Duly he brought his wife, driving her from Louisville in a carryall, a big rattling kind of vehicle. Piled in the back were boxes and baggage and two Negro slaves. But Pardue died suddenly, of an enlarged spleen, before the people of Luray had rightly got to know him.

When he first arrived, there was plenty of speculation at Buckley's store by the local cracker-barrel sages. "I heern he's a shady horse-trader," said one. "Made a pile of money in Kaintuck, but had to clear out."

"That's not the way I heern it," said another. "Made his money in whiskey. Married a high genteel gal, and she was turned out by her pa. Wonder what they's doin' hyer in Staunton?"

Only in part were these quidnuncs right. Winston Pardue had inherited a fairly large sum of money from his mother. Having unsuccessfully wooed Della Courtland, a beautiful, rather delicate girl, in the face of parental anger, he later, as a man of substance deserving to make his name in the distillery business, renewed his suit. Still, Della's father refused him as a son-in-law. Winston had appealed to Della, who was in love, or thought she was. The two had eloped to Louisville. Eager to start a new life in a new environment, they had moved, a year later, into the tall white house on the Staunton road.

The death of her husband left Della Pardue alone, frightened for the future, with a moderate fortune at her command. In a short time, she was open to male blandishments and the prospect of protection.

The ne'er-do-well of Newmarket, a young Ham Corry, was a big, handsome fellow, but shifty as a weather-vane cock. He lost no time in ingratiating himself with Della as the two rocked on her porch. In countless ways did young Ham soothe the lonely woman. One day, they were married.

After a few years, Della bore Ham Corry a daughter. He had wanted a son, but he shrugged his shoulders to this, as he did to most things, and ambled out of the darkened bedroom to sit and smoke on the porch.

The child was named Henrietta, after Della's mother. Miss Hetty, as Mammy Duro and Domeny, the two Negro slaves, called her, shot up to notable proportions with breathtaking speed.

"Lor' me, Miss Hetty, yo's ony twelve yea's ole, an' yo's high as a chuch steeple. When yo gwine stop down?"

Hetty grinned broadly, tossing her head. Day after day, the last anyone in the house would see of the girl, until she returned for supper, was the thick taffy-colored braid of hair flying like a golden banner on the breeze as she streaked off into the woods. Where she went, what she did, nobody knew.

Hetty seldom visited any of the villages roundabout. Loiterers in Newmarket, Luray, or Staunton were mildly surprised whenever a yellow-haired girl in a print dress went dashing through the sleepy main street astride a shaggy horse, dust rising in clouds as she passed. "Dat's dat Corry chile," some lounging Negro would say. "She ain' lak no she round hyer. Wild-like."

It was not that Hetty Corry was wild. She was magnificently free.

One day, Hetty approached Mammy Duro, who was kneading bread in the summer kitchen. "Have you any glass jars or old jugs, anything to set jelly in? If you have, give 'em to me."

"Wha yo want set jelly fo? Any jelly set round hyer I does it."

"I want to." Hetty went down cellar and rummaged out a tin dipper and a few old cracked cups.

While exploring the woods, Hetty had stumbled upon a rusted iron pot; probably some trappers or loggers had used it to cook in. It was huge, and there was an iron tripod lying close by, half hidden in the grass. From that day on, Hetty had a mission in life. She made wild-grape jelly, masses of it. For all around in these woods and in the river bottoms over toward Charlottesville the trees and snake fences were hung with thick garlands of wild-grape vines.

Hetty made sallies into the yards of village houses, where, from dump heaps and trash piles, she scavenged all manner of utensils for her grape jelly. Then, in the hush of a deep forest glade, she stirred her bubbling purple grape juice, for hours sweetening it with wild honey—"bee sugar," as Mammy Duro called it.

Talk buzzed in the villages when housewives, opening their doors of an early morning, found jars of aromatic wildgrape jelly in odd vessels standing on their doorsteps. Hetty was repaying them for the old jars and cups she had filched.

When she found a slightly chipped but pretty bowl of pale-green china with roses scattered on it, she set jelly in it to give to her mother, whom she seldom saw these days. Della suffered from a painful back ailment and rarely left her room. Most of her time was spent on a couch beside the front window.

"Don' yo go botherin' Miss Della, chile. She ailes pow'ful bad today," Mammy Duro said.

"Where's Pa?" the girl asked.

Mammy Duro rolled her eyes until the whites gleamed. "Who know dat? Down de sto', I reckon. Sittin' by de cracker-ba'l. I feed 'im, dat all."

Her mother was pleased when Hetty took the bowl of jelly into the curtain-shaded room. "Why, Hetty! Did you make this?" Della tasted it. "It's delicious. There is no flavor like wild grape. I've always loved it." Looking intently at her daughter, the woman said, "What a tall girl you are, Hetty. And that thick braid of hair—so long you can sit on it. Just like your Grandmother Courtland."

After Hetty had gone, Della rested her head on her thin, blue-veined hand, murmuring, "So pretty, too. And so simple. I wonder what will become of her."

When Hetty was nineteen years old, her mother died. The girl's life remained almost unchanged. She still pilfered all the pots, pans, and crockery she could find for her jelly. Far in the forest, hidden by swaying vines, she went on brewing her grape juice, stirring in spoonfuls of golden honey. Sometimes she twined a cluster of grapes and leaves in her hair. Like a virgin priestess, she chanted songs, learned from Domeny and Mammy Duro, while she stirred.

When cold weather and rain came to the forest, Hetty had to stay indoors far more than she liked. She taught herself to read, after a fashion, but figures and sums eluded her. In the wild-grape season, she was happy and busy.

Ham Corry, always unimportant, became a nonentity in his daughter's life. For hours, the man sat rocking, rocking, rocking on the front porch. His once straight back was bowed now, and his sunken jaws drooled dark-brown rivulets of tobacco juice. Cold days he rested in the village store, buying just enough merchandise to "treat the boys" and assure his welcome in the circle of drones; he sat, silent, all the day long, with time out only for meals.

One day, Ham Corry, not so spry on his toes as he once was, got in the way of a horseshoe game. A shoe struck him on the head; he flopped down in the dust, and never knew what hit him.

A year before the outbreak of the War Between the States, a young cousin of Hetty's, Thaddeus Corry, from Blue Ridge country, came to live with her. He was a bright, engaging youth with an avid desire to learn. For a time, he and Hetty read all the books they could lay hands on. Thaddeus even taught his cousin to weave. Together they set up a loom, like one his grandmother had in her mountain cabin, back of Denby Forks Run, in the mountains.

"Sometime, Cousin Hetty, I'll take you there to see Grandmaw," Thaddeus said. "She's powerful old, but she weaves the best wool cloth in the state, or so she 'lows.''

Hetty nodded. "Yes, Thaddy, we'll go to the Blue Ridge. Just you and me."

But young Thaddeus did not take his cousin to visit Grandmaw Corry and her loom; he was conscripted into the Confederate Army, and Hetty never heard from him again. But he had left his mark on her heart. Hetty had felt a great affection—something she had never before experienced—for her red-cheeked cousin.

After the defeat of Stonewall Jackson in the Battle of the Banks, near Winchester, in 1862, an unnatural quiet settled over the house of Miss Hetty Corry. The villagers were mystified when she sent Mammy Duro and Domeny away. True they were both getting old, but not so old they couldn't manage what little was to be done around the place. Miss Hetty bought a small farm for the old slaves on the Mary-Ann Creek.

From then on, the house where Miss Hetty lived was shuttered tight. No flicker of light ever shone from the windows. Boards were nailed across the front door. The house and its inhabitants had never attracted many visitors; now no one came at all.

The jelly-making went on. In the grape season, Miss Hetty worked in the summer kitchen. She and Domeny had moved the big iron kettle from the forest into the kitchen before he was sent off.

The sorrel horse that used to carry Miss Hetty clattering through the villages was old and sway-backed now, but every once in a while she backed him into the thills of a buggy, cinched a few straps, crammed some jars of jelly and dilapidated crates of chickens into the back of the rig, and jogged off to Luray or Newmarket. She would sell her wares and use the money for supplies.

Miss Hetty was talked about in the stores. She dressed like a man. Her once golden hair, though still worn in a thick braid, was streaked with gray, and an old butternut-felt hat was pulled down over her ears. A long ulster, made of homespun of her own weaving, and baggy breeches stuffed into high boots comprised her costume, no matter what the weather or season.

Among the supplies she bought were two that caused much conjecture— laudanum pills and liniments. Old Doc Treller, sitting in Seth Gassaway's Emporium, in Staunton, shook his head after Miss Hetty left the shop clutching a bottle of Starr's Laudanum Pills in her hand. "What the hell does she do with all the liniment and laudanum she buys?" he said. "She's tough as bull's hide. I took care of her ma years ago. But Het hain't never had a sick day in her life that I ever hear tell of."

Seth Gassaway scratched his head and said, "Twice a week nowadays, she comes in here or goes to Bill Saunder's, in Luray. Always orders liniment or laudanum pills. And she lives alone, don't she?"

One day in late summer, a boy out trapping otters along Mary-Ann Creek was terrified to hear the bloodcurdling, choking screams of a person in mortal agony. He cowered against a tree as someone came crashing through the thorny underbrush. A man in most horrible distress burst through the branches onto the path, where, grasping a tree trunk, he stood swaying. From head to foot, the man was purple-red and glistening. Clawing at his mouth and eyes, uttering whimpering cries, the wretch sank down to the ground, clutched at the boy's feet, and then lay still. The next moment, Hetty Corry, wild-eyed, emerged through the brush, waving a shotgun. The boy took to his heels along the creek bank; as he ran, a shot rang out and a bullet whizzed past his ear.

The sheriff visited Hetty Corry's house that evening, but it was empty of any occupants. Search revealed a bedroom in the attic with every evidence of long occupancy by a sick person. Under the bed was a box of bloodstained bandages. Piles of sheets and mattress stuffing filled a corner. Dozens of bottles, some empty, others containing the residue of liniments, were ranged on shelves and tables.

In every room of the house stood crocks, jars, bowls and basins of wild-grape jelly. Most of them were fermented or covered with a furred crust of green mold. The smell of fermentation and carbolic acid pervaded the air.

In a bedroom probably used by Miss Hetty as her own stood a tall French armoire. Hanging inside, ragged and bloodstained, were the jacket, breeches, and cap of a rifleman of the Northern Army.

Three days later, the sheriff and a posse, gathered together from neighboring farms, found Miss Hetty Corry in the cabin she had given to Mammy Duro and Domeny. Mammy had been dead for years. Domeny was very old, but when, some time earlier, Miss Hetty had staggered through his door, crazy-eyed and muttering, he had taken care of her as if she were a child.

The old man met the sheriff in the doorway of his cabin. "Shariff, be gentle wid she. Almos' daid. T'ont be long. Po' Miz Hetty."

Stooping, the sheriff entered a cubbylike room. Lying on a pile of cornhusk sacks, covered by her old ulster, was Miss Hetty.

She raised her hand to the sheriff. "I'm dying. You're too late. I took poison." The woman turned her head away. "I'll be asleep soon. Then I'll join Harry."

The sheriff bent over her. "Who is Harry, Miss Corry? Where did he come from? Tell me about him."

Miss Hetty's eyes were dimming now. "I don't think I can talk much. I'm so drowsy. Harry was young, like Thaddy. He came from Pennsylvania. Badly hurt . . . escaped prisoner . . . I hid him . . . I nursed him . . . I loved him."

Her breathing almost stopped. Then she rallied and stirred. "He aimed to rob me and run away. He crept up on me with a rifle when I was boiling grapes." The eyes dimmed again. "I threw the juice in his face. Oh, God! I loved him."

The tired eyes closed, and Miss Hetty ceased to breathe.

People who have lived in the Corry house since Miss Hetty's death tell strange tales of her reappearance. She moves about the house at night rattling jars and crockery. In the morning, purple stains are found on the floor and shelves.

A woman is seen to walk up the stairs to the attic. She seems to be carrying a tray to a sickroom. The woman wears a long ulsterlike coat and high boots. Her hair hangs in a thick braid. Always she looks furtively over her shoulder.

Sometimes the sobbing of a man in pain issues from the room at the head of the stairs. When this occurs, a strong smell of carbolic acid hangs about the hall.

One man said that on a night when he was gigging for frogs in the swampy river meadow, he noticed a fire glowing in the depths of the woods. He moved closer and saw the outline of a tall, slender woman, with a wreath of grape leaves in her hair, bending over an iron pot. She seemed to be stirring some sort of brew. There was a bright fire under the pot, and the odor of wild grapes filled the night air. The man walked away. Then, intending to investigate further, he returned to the spot. No fire glowed. No pot of mysterious brew steamed. No woman stirred.

A young man courting his girl walked with her along a lane near Luray.

Suddenly a figure stepped out of the tree shadows and confronted them in a threatening manner. The woman was tall and wore a soldier's forage cap. Across her arm she carried an Army rifle. As she came menacingly toward the couple, they turned and fled.

If Miss Hetty Corry lived today, she might be hard put to find enough wild grapes to carry on her large-scale jelly-making. When the blight that killed multitudes of chestnut trees in the United States swept the land, a similar blight attacked the wild grapes of the countryside; they no longer grow in the rich profusion of bygone years.

The Woman Who
Would Not Die

MOONRISE PLANTATION, BAYOU GRAND SARA, 1815

THIS TALE concerns Dominique de Laboutré, a woman who became a legend while she was still alive. Her tenacity to remain alive has provided the framework for many stories of the Louisiana bayous. Madam de Laboutré y de Ovanda, as she styled herself, is reported to have lived to the age of a hundred and seven years. She has been dead for decades, but her memory is kept ever green, for no one, man or woman, in all Louisiana can match her history.

When Nicolas de Ovanda sailed into the harbor of Santo Domingo, to become governor after the ousting of the devious old satyr Bobadilla, he staggered on deck, got a blast of the tropical land breeze full in the face, and fell flat with prostration. His wife, lying in her sweat-saturated bed below deck, quietly rolled over and died from the heat, leaving a son who had been born during the voyage.

Santo Domingo, the gridiron of Hades, was cordially hated by the French and Spanish people forced to live there. A man who escaped the flames of the Inquisition only to be sent on a secular mission to Santo Domingo hung himself from a window of the governor's palace; a note pinned to his robe read, "The flames of Inquisition are balm compared to this miasma of heat."

One day, in the huge white house of a rich Spanish sugar planter, a female child named Dominique was born; she was a descendant of Nicolas de Ovanda. The event occurred during a terrific heat spell preceding the rainy season, when the household had reached the nadir of its resistance. An exhausted nurse at the

207

christening is supposed to have dropped the infant Dominique on her head. All present thought the child was dead. Not a bit of it. It was only the beginning of a career of close calls which brought to the indestructible Dominique a peculiar fame.

Little is known of the early life of this daughter of adversity. At that time, roughly 1770, the French and Spanish planters, who divided the island neatly in half, fought hard and often amongst themselves. Spaniards controlled the eastern half, French the western half. Then, in 1790, a real reign of terror began, with a wave of bloody and bitter slave uprisings. Some unpopular French families were wiped out, their property destroyed. However, the savagery was mostly against the Spanish overlords, who were notoriously cruel to their slaves.

In after years, when Dominique was living at Moonrise Plantation, she wrote in a journal the events that led up to the night drunken Negroes attacked her father's house, putting it to the torch and massacring all the other members of her family. From the journal, family documents, word-of-mouth narrations, and even lullabies and chants sung by plantation Negroes, we can reconstruct the tapestry of this fantastic woman.

"No, no, Dominique," her mother said, in a whisper from behind her fan. "You cannot go to the water today. The sun would kill you just walking there. It is at least half a mile." She sighed deeply. "In all my years of living in this scorching climate, I cannot remember such a chain of hot humid days. Your father tells me all work in the canebrakes has stopped. Five slaves died yesterday—natives, too. All we can do is remain absolutely still." She stopped to fan herself, then continued, "There is unrest in the Negro quarters. In the town of Bombacque, a voodoo woman proclaims the end of the world and the poor fools of natives are drinking heavily in anticipation of eternity. Tonight, I am told by Zula, the death dance may be performed."

The woman, pale and fat, looked away toward the slave cabins. "May the good God forbid that happening. Every time the slaves hear the drums, it sends them quite mad. When I think of that horrible massacre at Tonnelette! Mass madness, caused by rum and the death-dance drums. Do lie down again." Madam Mère de Ovanda sank deeper into the pillow stuffed hourly with fresh fern leaves dipped in water.

But her daughter, slim and equally pale, had not heard much of the woman's talk; her quick eyes had noticed unusual activity. At the end of a broad avenue of Lambo trees she glimpsed groups of black figures moving stealthily along the highway to Bombacque. From far off, her ears caught the beat of voodoo tomtoms. Glancing toward the lightly clad figure of her mother, Dominique saw she was deep in sleep.

All day the hot mist drifted in from the sea. All day the rise and fall of drumbeats continued at intervals. No slave on the plantation worked. At sunset, when Dominique walked down to the street of slave cabins, she found it deserted of all except the aged and a few babies sprawling in the dust.

Dinner was not served to the Ovandas. Anyone who wanted food went to the cooking quarters, where old Raquele, a Spanish-Negro servant long past her usefulness, scrabbled some fruit and cold fowl onto a plate. The house servants seemed to have turned themselves loose. Over all prevailed a listlessness that affected even the autocratic Pedro de Ovanda, who reclined silently on a rattan couch, his evening pipe falling from his slack fingers. The night, without stars or moon, consisted solely of stillness and heat.

The Ovanda family, five in number, went to the upper gallery; there, facing the sea, which stirred no more than a pool of lead, they attempted to sleep. Dominique, half drowsing, heard bats skimming low, swooping between the pillars of the gallery. Heavy-eyed, she more sensed than saw a spreading glow in the sky a mile or so away. She wondered if it was another plantation put to the torch.

Suddenly she became aware of an approaching clamor, a rising sound of human unrest, ominous and distinctly savage. As she roused herself, the night was split by uproar. A veritable deluge of drumbeats—rapid, rolling, thunderous—nearly drowned out the tribal chants of the slaves, which prefaced, Dominique knew, an uprising against their white masters. The girl, her brother Christoph, and her sister Sallé ran to the balustrade just as a mob of Negroes broke from the heavily foliaged planting around the house.

The blacks, men and women, carried torches and machetes. The leaping glare of light gave an ugly look to the sweat-dripping ebony bodies, some entirely naked, that surged up the steps. All was pandemonium. In a haze of fire, shrieks of terror, and stench of bodies, Dominique felt herself swept up into the arms of her brother as he fled along the gallery. The mob was intent on despoiling the house, and Christoph, bearing his sister, was somehow able, unobserved, to find a hidden path that led through the bushes and down to a cove, where he kept a small sailing boat. The frenzied slaves were now firing the house.

Christoph ran hard. Then borne to his ear was the soft "pad-pad-pad" of bare feet running parallel to his own. Lengthening his stride, Christoph raced toward the beach. As he reached the sand, with no trees to screen him, a Negro rushed at him, machete swinging high to descend in the slicing arc used by slaves in the canebrakes. Christoph, big and muscular for his eighteen years, flung his sister onto the sands and seized the forearm of the slave. Grappling with the man, he succeeded in stopping the swing of the machete, but the man dropped the weapon, and it fell across the shoulders of Dominique, cutting a gash in the side of her throat.

Hours later, Dominique, her head seemingly half severed from her body, and Christoph, dead from drowning, were found in the water of the cove by Amoran Lopez, who came by in his ship and picked up survivors of the uprising. When Lopez dragged the girl aboard, he was amazed that she lived. "Look, padre," he said to Abbé Santandar, standing near him. "The gash is washed clean of blood by the sea. By God's grace, no artery is severed. It is Pedro de Ovanda's daughter. That drowned boy was her brother, Christoph."

The Abbé examined the wound in Dominique's throat. "From a machete, certainly. I have never seen the like of this, my son. It is the salt water that has stopped the flow of blood and, in a manner, cauterized the wound."

The wound in the throat of Dominique Lanos-de Ovanda never completely healed. It showed even at the age of thirty, when she became the wife of Gaston Laboutré, of New Orleans.

The marriage between Gaston and Dominique was contracted simply because Dominique was an aristocrat, and Gaston wanted a super-governess for his three daughters, brought forth by a lowborn mistress. By marrying the emigrée from Santo Domingo, he avoided having to pay her wages. No more miserly man ever trod the earth than Gaston Laboutré.

Often, in the years of her marriage, Dominique was reduced to a nervous frenzy by her husband's tirades. Usually he accused her either of not being interested in his daughters or of gross extravagance. During such scenes, the wound across her throat grew discolored and bled. This was not all she had to bear.

More than once, Gaston, or a man hired by him, tried to murder Dominique. Laboutré had hoped that when the slave uprisings in Santo Domingo were quelled and the sugar plantations were worked again, Dominique would inherit a worth-while fortune. But the settling of island affairs proved a long, involved business. So great was the destruction at the Lanos-de Ovanda plantation that what was left was incorporated into government enterprise. With the changing of political factions, Madam Laboutré received almost nothing from her confiscated estate—reason enough for murder, in Gaston's mind. Later on, his desire to be rid of her increased when he wanted to replace his governess-wife with a voluptuous quadroon from Rampart Street, who was knowledgeable as well as bedworthy. Here again Gaston was casting for governess as well as wife.

When Dominique arrived at New Orleans, on the refugee ship captained by Amoran Lopez, she entered the Hospital of the Ursulines. Abbé Santandar visited her almost daily.

As soon as the wound in her throat had healed somewhat and her strength allowed walking abroad, he secured a post for the girl in a perfume establishment. It was there that Gaston Laboutré, buying a present for one of his numerous Rampart Street *placée* acquaintances, first saw the tall, golden-haired young woman whose air of elegant detachment and melodious speaking voice took his fancy. If at the time he also noticed that she wore a rose silk scarf wrapped tightly around her throat, it did not signify. What did hold his attention was the magnificent emerald, set in pearls and diamonds, that held the scarf in place. The brooch whetted his curiosity.

"Pardon, mademoiselle, that is a most beautiful brooch pinning your kerchief. It is very rich, is it not, to wear so openly? There are scoundrels all about, you know."

Dominique looked at the rather rakish man who had spoken to her. "Oh, monsieur, you are kind to admire. It is the only brooch I have. I was wearing it the night I was"—the girl's face saddened—"the night I left Santo Domingo. Do not fear. On the street, I cover the brooch with my scarf."

Dominique had not properly recovered from her wound, and she was forced to leave the perfume shop. The widower of Moonrise plantation had been flattering and serious in his attentions. Abbé Santandar advised that she accept his proposal.

"Monsieur Laboutré is a vastly rich planter. His family is distinguished. Moonrise stands far out on the Bayou Grand Sara. There you will soon regain your health. Yes, my daughter, I advise it."

At first, Dominique reveled in the beauty of the bayou. The vast stretches of cypress and magnolia enchanted her. However, none of her three ugly, dark-browed stepdaughters, ranging in age from seven years to fifteen, appealed to her. Sullen, spiteful to one another and to their stepmother, they were an unappetizing trinity of girls.

Indeed, in the large, oddly assorted family of Laboutré, no one appeared to like anyone else; temperamental affinity did not exist. Three old aunts of Gaston's, sisters of his deceased mother, lived in a kind of dusky dormitory under the eaves of Moonrise. An incredibly ancient stepfather, named de la Motte, whose tenuous existence was sustained in the garçonnière at the end of a magnolia alley, sang quavering French ditties constantly, venturing into the house only for meals. Sometimes, in the night, Dominique would be awakened by pitiful cries coming from the old man's quarters. Rumors of a huge mulatto woman servant beating the poor fellow were rife.

It was during one of these nocturnal disturbances that Gaston tried, the first time, to kill his wife. In the dark, Dominique sat up in bed, listening to the beseeching pleas of "Stop! No, no! Please, Phao, no more!" As she debated whether or not to intervene, she was suddenly flung upon her back with a pillow pounded down over her face. Though she fought with all her might, the smothering woman lost consciousness. Only when a murky dawn lighted the jalousies did she revive.

In the morning, pale and weak, she entered the dining room, where the family were assembled. A heavy white cloth was wrapped around her throat; over one side of the cloth spread a dark-red stain. A gasp, a startled look of disbelief in the eyes of Gaston as he half-rose from his chair proved to Dominique who the pillow wielder had been.

A few months passed. One day, just at sunset, Gaston arrived at the house riding a handsome sorrel mare; he rode, romantically, beside the family barouche. Ensconced behind the French lacquered doors sat a brazenly beautiful quadroon, Melanie Fourchmon, late of Rampart Street. Though she was ostensibly a governess for the Laboutré daughters, her position in the household left nothing to the imagination. From the first, Melanie treated Madam Laboutré as nothing, frequently remarking in front of people, "It is time she either bled to death with that horrible wound or somebody finished the job started in Santo Domingo." When Gaston, in a drunken moment, added to her comment, "Why don't you do it?" she smiled and shrugged. "I do not like the sight or smell of blood. There are, *au fond,* other means, no?"

The second attempt against Dominique's life was a carefully planned carriage accident. Sometimes of an afternoon, she liked to drive about the roads into meadow lanes where pink-and-ivory-petaled mallow bloomed in great abundance. An old half-blind mare called Dorinia ambled between the shafts of the basket phaeton Dominique used; she enjoyed the pleasant leisurely pace of the animal. One spring day, when dog-tooth violets lined the roadway, Dominique was surprised, emerging from under the portico, to see a restive bay-gelding in Dorinia's place. A young black boy held the bridle. He grinned widely and doffed his cap. "Madam Laboutré, missa, I's to ride de back ob Valour today. Ole Dorinia she ailin'. Jes' step yo'sef into de ca'ige please, missa."

Hardly glancing at the bay-gelding, Dominique settled comfortably among the linen cushions in the basket seat. Unconsciously, her hand went to her throat, tightly wrapped in a silk scarf. The wound, throbbing, pained her slightly. It was hot today, unusually hot for April.

As the phaeton sped along at a smart pace, the postilion swung his mount into a lane with an arch of trees that cast a lattice pattern of deep shadow. At the end of his road, Dominique recalled, lay a deep gully where an abandoned stone quarry had once been worked. She was about to call out to the boy to go slower on the rutted road when a shot rang out from some tamarind bushes bordering the roadside. The boy screamed, clutched at his side, and toppled from the saddle while the frightened gelding reared and plunged ahead. They tore along the road, the carriage swaying perilously from side to side, grazing the tree trunks. Dominique leaned over the dashboard to catch the reins, but realized there were no long reins such as she used for old Dorinia; only bridle reins flapped on the maddened horse's neck. She was trying to regain her seat when a wheel struck a big rough-cut stone, once quarried but now lying concealed in rank grass. The woman was thrown clear, but the horse plunged over the side of the quarry, dragging the phaeton behind him.

Dominique lay unconscious in the grass for hours. At nightfall, an overseer and some field hands, returning to Belle Morrie plantation along the quarry road, found her. The overseer cried, "Fo' God, hit's Madam missa from Moonrise! She daid? Run, yo' Clemente boy, git help quick!"

Many weeks passed while Dominique Laboutré lay miserably in pain in a room at Moonrise. Her spine had been badly hurt, and again the wound in her throat was almost in a state of hemorrhage. At times, her life was despaired of.

Only through the close attention of Samba, an old Cajun Negro woman, who felt compassion for this unwanted wife and hated arrogant Melanie, did Dominique survive.

The third, and last, attempt to kill his wife cost Gaston and his quadroon mistress their own lives. About a year after the runaway near the stone quarry, Melanie changed her attitude toward Dominique. Gaston had given his enamorata a pleasure barge of carved and filigreed wood. It was much the fashion of persons dwelling along the bayous to give picnics on the water. Sometimes the barges were decked with flowers: often music was provided. One morning, Melanie approached Dominique, who was sitting on the upper gallery.

"Bon, madam. It is so fine, the weather. Monsieur your husband desires we make a small gala on the bayou, no? Tomorrow or the next day? You will accompany us? It will be the family, yes?"

Dominique swept Melanie with her eyes, hesitated, then responded to this friendliness. "Yes, I will come. The banks are filled with pink mallow, my favorite flower. It will be good."

But on the next day a mass of heat shut down on the bayou and surrounding countryside. Then a cloudburst washed the flowers away. When the air cleared, a dismal, rain-matted vista of bayou and sodden Spanish moss lay on every hand. Melanie persisted, however, in her desire to hold the picnic.

At first, Dominique, thinking of the ruined flowers, objected. Then Gaston intervened. "Why is it you treat Melanie so rudely?" he said. "She tries always to include you when we go abroad. You complain of loneliness. It's your own fault entirely."

To end the reprimanding, Dominique said, "I will go. But the damp heat out on the open bayou may cause my malaria to return, and my throat wound throbs today almost beyond bearing." Dominique was aware that the throbbing was almost a barometer of ill chance; each time disaster had threatened, the wound had ached miserably. But she allowed herself to be driven to the pier that jutted into the bayou at the end of the magnolia walk.

Once aboard the barge, Dominique was surprised, and more than a little dismayed, to see that none of the aunts or old D'Arbet de la Motte, Gaston's senile stepfather, was aboard. When questioned, Gaston said, "The heat and their age crept upon my revered family. Indeed, Tante Adèle is bedded. We will go far out to the mouth of the bayou. It may be cooler there."

Dominique felt a curious feeling run through her body at the thought of heading for the far, misty reaches of the bayou with her husband and his mistress as companions. Hebo, an old toothless Negro, bleary-eyed with liquor, was the only crew she could see.

For a while, all went well. A delicious lunch, including wine, was served on deck under the awning. A hot wind from the canebrakes filled the sail, and the barge made good headway toward the bayou mouth. After lunch, the three voyagers settled into deck chairs, preparing for the inevitable afternoon siesta. Dominique felt unnaturally drowsy and her neck muscles palpitated violently. Then she remembered that Gaston had poured her a special glass of wine—doubtless containing drug. She felt it creeping through her veins. Then her ears began to buzz, and soon added to it was another sound—the screech of wind, suddenly sprung up across the flat expanse of water. Above it all rose the voices of Gaston and Melanie shouting orders to Hebo.

The next thing Dominique knew, she was floating in the reedy fringes of a tiny inlet in the arms of a dead man. Somehow the old slave Hebo had managed to save her. He had swum to the shore before he died, for one arm was clasped tightly around her waist, the other caught in a bunch of reed fronds. Of the barge, Gaston, and Melanie, there was no trace; only the hot night air, the tepid water, and trillions of misty stars above remained.

Dominique struggled back to the plantation and afterward suffered a long bout of malaria and lung fever that would have killed anybody but the invincible Madam Laboutré. Weeks later, the shark-raddled bodies of Gaston and Melanie were found. The storm had swamped the barge in no time, according to fishermen who themselves had been all but destroyed in the vicinity. Dominique inherited Moonrise, and for the first time in her adult life she felt the power of wealth and great land holdings.

One by one, the old pensioners died. The three aunts expired a year or so apart, according to their age. Old stepfather D'Arbet lingered on, almost a wraith: finally a pirogue filled with mimosa carried his body to the de la Motte family cemetery at Allure plantation, down the bayou.

Of the three daughters of Gaston Laboutré, little is known except of Marguerite, the eldest. She married Ronce de Pargarrie, a weakling second son from Golden Horn plantation, near Donaldsonville. He came to Moonrise, eked out an ineffectual life, and was constantly dominated by his shrewish wife.

In the last years of Dominique's life journey, only she, Marguerite, now a widow, and Laurelie, Marguerite's sickly daughter, lived shuttered away behind the green jalousies of the huge, echoing house. Then, having lived over a century, against man's devious attempts to kill her, Dominique Lanos-de Ovanda Laboutré expired from internal hemorrhages. A doctor summoned hurriedly from St. Francisville later wrote a friend that the condition of Madam Laboutré's corpse was extraordinary. The wound on her throat, which had never properly healed and had often bled externally, had, at the end, spurted internally like a rich crimson fountain.

After the death of Dominique, Moonrise plantation sank almost into desuetude. Later, Marguerite's invalid daughter Laurelie, at the age of twenty, died of fright, or so a servant proclaimed loudly.

"Yess'm, yass'm, she did," said the frightened Negro woman. "She'm jes set up screechin', 'Dat hant agin! Dat's ole Dominique covered im blood!' she say, An den missa Laurelie she cave in an die quick."

A doctor performed an autopsy and confirmed the woman's opinion. The staring eyes, slack jaw, tense muscles, and absence of blemish or contortion of the intestines pointed to death by heart failure.

Both the slave and the doctor were undoubtedly right. Soon after Dominique's funeral, when her body was placed in a table tomb under the live oaks at Moonrise cemetery, her ghost had taken to walking abroad. Late dusk, sunset and early morning seemed to be the times most favored by the erstwhile mistress of the plantation. Slaves who encountered her apparition ran howling to their cabins to hide. She was seen prowling on the galleries at rise of moon, white draperies floating for yards about her—a style from girlhood days in Santo Domingo that she had worn all her life.

Always the woman seemed vastly distraught. Both hands grasped her throat, which was swathed in silk folds. At times the bandage was virgin white, more often saturated with blood.

The most curious of all Dominique's manifestations, to my mind, is the story of the bloodstained tablecloth. Miss Louisa Butler, of Cottage plantation, near St. Francisville, recognized as a most inveterate and interesting historian of Louisiana, relates this story. It appears that while Dominique lived, she was always first at table, no matter how charged with emotion the atmosphere was; though a family divided against itself growled and spat around her chair for three generations, the mistress of Moonrise always came to the table except during illness.

One morning after Dominique's death, Madam Marguerite and her daughter, at breakfast, were discussing a suitor who wished to pay his respects to the frail, lonely Laurelie. Marguerite was adamant. "That fortune hunter will not enter this house! He expects you to die at any time. Don't be such a fool!"

This tirade, and more, sent the unhappy girl into hysterics. Suddenly quieting, she grasped the arms of her chair, calling to her mother. "Look! Look, there where Madam Dominique always sat!" On the tablecloth in front of the empty chair spread an angry stain of blood.

The Longest Boy
in Tennessee

MEMPHIS, 1845

THE LENGTHENING shadows of approaching twilight that cross-hatched the muddy waters of the narrow Pentee River, a few miles from Memphis, cast a shadow of fear across the heart of Cuff, a little black boy who had spent the afternoon, with a line tied to his great toe, fishing for a bullhead or a mud-flatty. He had just wakened, startled, from one of the long, dreamless naps that qualified him for the open championship in Pentee Basin for standing, sitting, or prone dozing. His eyes seemed enormous and all whites as he hastily gathered his can of bait and piece of catgut line.

Glancing quickly up and down the fast-darkening bank of the river, the boy set off at a rapid trot toward his mammy's cabin in the canebrake. "Sho' nuf I shoulda lit out f'um dat riber fo' de black night come," Cuff muttered to the worms writhing in the can he held to his skinny breast. "Haunts is thicker'n sand flies in dis yere woods. Dat ole tall man, he still markin' de trees wid a rake's haid."

Suddenly the little black boy froze in mid-lope, one foot raised like a pointer. From the very bowels of his shivering frame came the whispering words "Fo' God—God, dar he is."

And there he was—the Tall Man, as the apparition of Raike Gaston is known to frequenters of the woods and canebrakes, the green savannahs, and the sumac-

219

drifted foothills of the Great Smokies of Tennessee. The immensely tall shade, a length of stature approaching the improbable, strode along, becoming one with the rough trunks of soaring butternut and ash trees. Cuff, immobile in fascinated terror, might have been a stunted blackthorn scrub. The Tall Man stopped only once before he disappeared down a wood path into the gloom of a thicket. He paused to carve, in swift, jagged lines, a crudely drawn rake head, a symbol that has marked countless trees and forests, even within the walled gardens of plantations, in half the states below the Mason and Dixon Line.

The roaming ghost of Raike seems never to rest. For three decades, he has frightened the wits out of Negroes of all ages who inhabit the Mississippi River lands, even though they know he would never harm them. Timid young ladies in plantation gardens, pungent with myrtle and verbena, have swooned at the sight of the towering man in shrunken butternut jeans. Keepers of crossroad stores in the Blue Ridge Mountains and the Cumberlands have discovered him lounging on the steps of the store porch, carving his eternal rake head into a post. Many a man will proudly show you the carving.

One chilly night, four trappers in the Appalachians wrapped themselves in blankets and lay down close to the banked pine-knot fire. During the night, one of the four heeding a call of nature, was puzzled to see a fifth figure stretched out, feet to the embers. A mighty long man, it seemed to the trapper. Well, the stranger was asleep. He'd talk to him in the morning. When dawn broke and the trappers stirred, no fifth man, long or short, was stretched in front of the fire. But a design in the shape of a rake head had been dug into the soft earth.

On a crisp morning of early spring in the year 1810, a tall young man, mounted upon a large gray Thoroughbred hunter, went out between the creeper-wreathed stone gate posts of Bellebois plantation. Onto the Memphis highway toward the wide world and high adventure rode Forbes Gaston.

It was early for the heir to Bellebois to be abroad. Usually, after a long session at the card table, with many a bottle of claret and, as the night grew old, whiskey toddies consumed, the head of Forbes was a monument to Bacchus until the sun climbed high.

This morning was different. As Forbes, sitting lithe and graceful in his light-weight English saddle, confided to the twitching ears of Gray Eagle, "I've decided that I'm hiding my light under a bushel. I'm a *very* talented man at cards. Memphis isn't big enough for a man of my talent. Neither are the dives along the river—the danger from cutthroats is greater than the gains, and the stink revolts me. If I am to be a Mississippi gambler, I shall be one with style." Gray Eagle understood his master. Nodding his black-crested head, curvetting and charming, he approved. Horse and rider took the river road at a fast pace through the early-morning mist.

Somewhere along the way, the Goddess of Chance, spry and fickle Jezebel, sprang aboard the broad rump of Gray Eagle. Riding pillion, her arms encircled the muscular waist of Forbes Gaston. Into his ear she whispered, "I shall favor you above all others . . ."

Up and down the Mississippi ranged Forbes Gaston, known to all men as a gambler with diabolical luck. To the women he encountered in his journey along the pleasure-seeking waterway, he was an insatiable lover. He was tall and well built, and he dressed inevitably in pearl-gray or plum-colored broadcloth, with rich jewelry of the period, sparsely but elegantly displayed; he wore his dark red hair in waves over his high forehead. Those who looked into the narrow steel-blue eyes of Forbes Gaston, across a card table or in the candlelight of a bedchamber, never forgot him.

For three years, the Goddess of Chance held strictly to the letter of her promise. One night, Forbes played a hunch and left the riverboat Bellamey Star at Alton, where the Missouri River flows into the Mississippi. He had heard that the best showboats and dance halls anywhere along the river were to be found in this wide-open town, known at the time as Alton River Forks.

An aging riverboat gambler had invited Forbes to drink with him on the trip down the river from Rock Island. Professor Dandridge, as the man was known, related tall tales of the joys to be found in Alton River Forks. "The women in the dance halls are the purtiest you'll find outside of N'Orleans, and the damned refinedest," the professor said, rubbing his hands together. Refined women did not particularly appeal to Forbes; in fact he liked big-boned brazen wenches with tremendous staying power, which is precisely what he got in Alton River Forks.

His first night there, Forbes visited the showboats, the dance halls, and a brothel or two. By sunrise he had lost a few hundred dollars, a distinctly new experience for the gambler from Bellebois plantation.

Unlike many river gamblers, Forbes never assumed a fictitious name, for he was still heir to Bellebois and intended to return there to end his days. Meantime, gambling was his career. Someday, however, he expected to marry, settle down, and sire an heir.

After a few days in Alton, Forbes was about ready to take passage on the Belle Rosemond, a handsomely appointed new river steamer, to sample the gaming rooms and amatory pleasures of Baton Rouge. The Belle Rosemond, gleaming like a white, crimson, and gold jewel casket, had tied up at Forks wharf at sundown; the journey down the river was to continue at midnight. Forbes decided to while away his last few hours in Alton by visiting the one dance hall he had not seen during his stay. It was called the Golden Whirl and was run by a former singer, named Paillard, from the French Opera in New Orleans.

Paillard had been caught in the toils of the law for raping the young daughter of a planter and had been forced to flee New Orleans. But he did not go alone. He brought his mistress along with him; in her big, richly curved body and the depths of her amber cat's eyes lay, unknown to both concerned, the future of Forbes Gaston.

The Golden Whirl dance hall occupied a three-story square building of whitewashed logs a little outside of town. As Forbes approached the place, he noticed that it lived up to its name; it was lighted from cellar to roof by festoons of candles set in transparent yellow globes and jars. A veritable nimbus of golden light transformed a building that in the cold light of day was a dejected, overblown log cabin.

Pushing open the gilded entrance door, Forbes found himself in the midst of hundreds of dancers gliding or stepping past him. He turned towards the long bar that occupied one side of the room and halted to watch the leisurely progress of a woman who was coming down the curved stairway at the back of the hall. Although he had, in his career, observed many kinds of female lure in many states of enticement, he had never seen a sight like this.

Forbes saw a tall, broadly made woman of thirty years or so, dressed in rich gold-colored satin. Masses of bright-yellow hair were piled in innumerable puffs and curls above her wide forehead and murky amber eyes. She was heavily rouged, and her bosom, throat, and fingers were covered with cheap diamonds; in one hand she waved a yellow heron-feather fan. The whole picture was one of outrageous flamboyance. For a moment, Forbes Gaston could scarcely believe his eyes. Then he smiled to himself and said, "Messalina—a monument to lust. Brash and tarnished as all hell. But I want her and I'll have her."

So the gambler met the Golden Whirl, a name she had used since her younger, more glamorous days in New Orleans bordellos. Together they found a secluded table near the stairs and drank to their meeting. For a few moments, the two looked at each other, appraisingly. Then Forbes asked, "What's your name?"

In a throaty voice, trailing the echo of countless whiskeys, the woman replied, "Nan."

"Nan what?"

The woman made a gesture that seemed to brush the diamonds away from her immense bosom as if they were crumbs. "Diamonds, I guess. That's what he calls me. Pierre, I mean. I was born Raike. Nan Raike."

Forbes was silent. Then he leaned close to her and said, "I am going to Baton Rouge tonight on the Belle Rosemond. You are going with me. I'll marry you in Baton Rouge."

For some years, Forbes and Nan Gaston roamed the river. During the first few months, they were sometimes only a few miles ahead of Pierre Paillard, of the Golden Whirl, who was loudly vehement about the elopement and out to kill both Nan and Forbes if he so much as laid eyes on them. He claimed that the diamonds Nan had walked out wearing were worth a fortune—his fortune. Forbes could easily have burst his bubble, for he found out early that the lot were the sorriest kind of paste, not even the beautiful French *paillon* so fashionable at the time. In fact, Nan's armor of diamonds was practically worthless.

Finally, in 1814, Pierre died and the chase was off. The Gastons settled in New Orleans.

There stood on Bourbon Street a private house where gambling for high stakes started at sundown and lasted until dawn. Early one morning, when only a few people were abroad, on their way to Mass, a half-demented man stumbled down the steps. This man, La Moyre D'Estange, had, until an hour before, been master of Marmont, a beautiful plantation halfway between New Orleans and Lake Pontchartrain. Forbes had won the place lock, stock and barrel, and the Gastons promptly moved in and took over.

During the first year at Marmont, a boy was born to the Gastons. Nan was indifferent, Forbes elated. No women visited the plantation, but men of various classes of society tethered their horses in front of the handsome double verandahs. New Orleans gossips vowed that the stakes of the gambling parties at

Marmont were as high as those called on the night D'Estange lost his heritage to the new owner.

As a mother, Nan Raike Gaston proved to be a failure. A woman who had flourished as a uniquely gifted prostitute in New Orleans bordellos at the age of fifteen had little mental or emotional equipment for motherhood. She hated every phase of maternity and said so in no uncertain terms. But she pleased virile Forbes Gaston to the hilt. That was her métier, and she made the most of it.

Happily, the son, Raike Gaston, never suffered for attention. Marmont plantation provided black nurses of varying ages who, almost from his birth, took the place of his feckless, increasingly blowzy mother. Raike grew rapidly to a huge size, as expansive in his ways as he was big in build. Like his father, he sprouted a mane of red hair, but Raike's was fiery red. In all ways, Raike inherited his mother's proclivities, with the added beauty of wide good nature and abundant humor. When he ran away from Marmont, at the age of twelve, to range the world according to his own lights, he was a veritable colossus in build, with fleshly appetites to complement his proportions.

Meanwhile, the Goddess of Chance had ended her vigilance. The once vital and brilliant adventurer, Forbes Gaston, of Marmont and Bellebois plantations, sank into a lecherous, besotted life. It ended in untimely death, for him and for Nan, during the plague that swept New Orleans during the summer of 1826.

The progress of ever-smiling redheaded Raike assumed some of the characteristics attributed to Tyll Eulenspiegel, and to the Hogarthian rips and rake-helly bloods of eighteenth-century Ireland. Still, he remained a simple fellow with country tastes. He shunned cities, in the main, seeking shaded forest glades and sunny valleys, country farms and small villages. A chronicler of Johnny Appleseed, to whom I related the improbably amorous life journey of Raike Gaston, chuckled at its conclusion, and said, "He might almost be called the Johnny Appleseed of the hedgerows, the hay mows, and the farmsteads. He sowed a crop of youngsters—the apples of infidelity."

It is said that when Raike Gaston reached the age of eighteen, he stood six feet ten inches in his bare feet. At country fairs, square dances, church socials and revival meetings, Raike shone brightly. His brawn suited his height. He could take on any two men for fisticuffs or wrestling. He could perform feats of strength such as lifting and throwing animals. He ate and drank prodigiously. While consuming quarts of deadly back-still liquor, Raike would smile as good-humoredly as ever. When he went along mountain paths in Tennessee and the Cumberlands, or down into the Shenandoah Valley, he was always being invited to drink somebody's private brand, to prove to less stalwart souls how fine and harmless the brew actually was. Raike became a notable connoisseur, to the extent that in later life, when he hid out in a cave in the Great Smokies for two years, to elude an irate sheriff whose wife had tried to run off with him, he set up a still of his own that became famous.

A story is told that during Raike's enforced cave life, some of the friends whom he supplied with pot brew saw the irate sheriff and a posse coming up the mountain. To discourage the law, the men stood every few hundred yards along the steep path; as the sheriff and his posse came abreast of each watcher, they were offered a jug of liquor to help them on their way. It was Raike Gaston's most potent brew, and, needless to say, the law never reached the hideaway cave.

Another story is told of a conversation that took place in Newmarket, in the Shenandoah Valley, between Raike and a gospeler who rode the mountains, preaching along the way. It was a hot summer day. Raike—barefoot, stripped to the waist, and wearing a pair of tight, shrunken butternut breeches—walked along the dusty main street of the somnolent village. Suddenly he let out a yell fit to shatter the stalactites in the nearby caverns of Luray. "I'm thirsty!" he bellowed. "Where are all you gals with something to drink?"

Instantly the village sprang to life. From every house along the street, women rushed out with a jug or pitcher of something cool and wet. At their heels ran a litter of children of assorted ages. Crowding around the nearly naked tower of sun-browned Raike Gaston, the women purred and slithered.

As he was quenching his well-known thirst, Raike spied the local gospeler riding toward him on a leggy mule. With a swooping motion of his arms, Raike swung two gaping children off their feet into the air. Placing a resounding kiss on each startled child's face, Raike lowered them to the dusty road and repeated the performance with two more children, and so on, until he had kissed nearly every child in sight. Then he turned to the frowning dominie and held out his immense brown paw. "Now I can shake your hand!" he roared. "You see, I always have to kiss any child I see in these parts—fatherly affection like, for I've passed this way many times before."

At twenty-five, Raike Gaston was becoming part of the folklore of the area, though the chances are fair that he never sensed it. The towering, brightly shining man, with the bellowing voice, the infectious laugh, the cockscomb of fiery hair, and the disposition of a ramping stallion, held the eye of every man, woman, and child who ever came within sight of him. Countless stories were told in taverns and village greens about him. Jingles were quoted, some even set to music. Indeed his life became a kind of saga.

All his days, women of every station adored him. Babies he snatched from play and tossed high in the air until they were breathless with wonder. Children worshipped him. Admiring boys accompanied him on hunting trips. Raike Gaston became a symbol of freedom and joy of life.

His relations with women, according to tales I have heard recounted, were free and unfettered. He had an air of courtliness in approaching his amours that may have come from being sired by a virile aristocrat out of a rough-cast harlot. He treated the lady of a grand plantation, met clandestinely in garden or summerhouse, in a wildly passionate, yet tender manner. Simple, cowlike creatures, whom he surprised in remote cabins or farms and literally swept off their feet, were meted the same treatment. Jaded, razzled whores of the riverside stews, sodden by endless debaucheries, found new life and enjoyment in the arms of the unfastidious Raike.

On a day of steaming heat and plaguing gnats, Raike came out of a forest of sycamores onto the cress-bordered bank of a small shaded river in Tennessee. It was such a cool and inviting spot that he stripped himself and plunged into the water. For a while, he just luxuriated in the forest silence and the cool depths of the pool.

Finally, refreshed beyond measure, Raike scrambled up the bank and stood for a while, idly chewing on a sprig of sharp-tasting water cress. Stark naked, like a towering bronze statue of some Attic god, he stood, oblivious to all but his feeling of well-being. Suddenly a cackle of laughter rang out from the fringe of ferns on the opposite bank of the narrow stream. An old Negro woman who was standing there, hands on her hips, regarding him. "Boy, boy," she called, shaking her head. "Take me hebenward effen yo' ain't de longest boy in Tennessee."

Raike threw back his head and let out a mighty shout of laughter that rang through the forest aisles. The old woman hefted a sack onto her scrawny shoulder and limped off into the greenery. Listening, Raike heard the rise and fall of a curious kind of song, almost a chant.

Take me up, Lord, fo' I am free
Take me up, Lord, Lord, fo' I done see
A critter high as de topmos' tree
Dat longest boy in Tennessee.

With the years, the verses of this song multiplied to fit various situations in widely scattered localities. But the stanzas always finished with the two lines

A critter high as de topmos' tree
Dat longest boy in Tennessee.

Many a weary young soldier, marching through ankle-deep dust or slogging through interminable mud with the Confederate Army, sang the rousing marching song, "The Longest Boy in Tennessee." The simple song of a life of shining freedom must have put new heart into the singer.

Raike became so popular in the states where he traveled that many a tavern on frequented highways, as well as remote bed-me-downs in Arkansas and Kentucky, hung out signs picturing a tall, redheaded man stalking along, carrying a garden rake. The signs were painted by itinerant artists, the portrait painters of the countryside who gave us what we now call American primitives. The tavern names varied little—the Roamer, the Tall Traveler, the Rake in Hand. One tavern, ambitious for the quality trade, on the posting road between Charleston and Columbia, South Carolina, put a bark of wit into its sign—the Great Producer.

On Raike Gaston's twenty-ninth birthday, he sat late into the night, in a tavern near Chattanooga, with a traveler from Memphis. When the man heard his companion's name, he snorted. "Humph! So you're Raike Gaston. A long while back you should've struck out fer your inheritance. Shame to you, lettin' a fine plantation like Bellebois go to ruin."

Raike sprang up from the bench he was straddling. Grabbing the speaker's wrist, he said, "Ruin? Where are the Gastons to let Bellebois fall to ruin? I ain't never been there. Where's it lay?"

The next morning, Raike and the traveler set out for Bellebois. The man rode a craggy horse hardly fit to travel, but Raike preferred to walk. His long legs were so used to reducing the forest leagues, that he found himself, half the time, ahead of the nag.

The day Raike walked up the rutted, weed-grown avenue of live oaks to the portico of Bellebois was much the same kind of sparkling spring day as when his father rode Gray Eagle out onto the river road to seek his fortune. But it was a woefully different house now. Clematis, wisteria, and jasmine vines, run riot, had pulled the slender columns of the verandahs all awry. Myrtle, dogrose, heliotrope, and climbing roses had become a tangle of dead branches. Once glistening white, the house looked dirty and mildewed; rust and green stains from the copper roof drains added to the general air of dejection.

Raike walked around to the slave street, where a few cabins remained upright, but many had fallen into a heap of jumbled brick and stucco. "So, this is the beautiful Bellebois my father used to tell me about," Raike said to his companion. "This derelict is my fine inheritance. I don't want it. I want my cool, fragrant forests, my singing brooks and silvery rivers. I want my roof to be mountains and massy clouds, and my bed the green of farmed valleys."

Just as Raike was turning to leave, a high, rasping voice from the upper verandah shouted, "Stop!"

He swung around and looked up. There stood a thin scarecrow of a man, with a stained old bed quilt thrown over his shoulders. The raspy voice continued, "Who are you? Get off my place anyhow. Git afore I call the hounds." Then, as Raike stared silently at the man, the voice rose to a frightened whine. "Yer Gaston, I can see that. Ye can't have Bellebois. No, no, ye can't. It's mine fair an' square. Never was no will. I was next—" The old man turned and fled into the room behind him. As Raike spat into the dust in disgust, he heard a high shriek issue from somewhere in the tottering house. "Ajax! Ajax, set the hounds out! Set 'em out quick!"

Later that day, from a lawyer in Memphis, Raike learned that when his father died of plague in New Orleans, he had either made no will or, if he had, it could not be found. For ten years, the lawyer had searched for Forbes' son, for he was known to have had one. But well known as Raike was in many states, he never had been found. The plantation, which even at Forbes Gaston's death was in a bad state, went to a Gaston uncle, an old invalid, who lived in Nashville. There it was.

Raike listened attentively to the lawyer's story. Then he rose to his astonishing height and threw up his arms, rattling the glass prisms of a high-hanging chandelier. "I don't want the place," he said. "Let the old critter die in it. Then burn it to the ground."

For a year after this little venture into civilization, Raike's progress along the banks of the Mississippi resembled a conflagration. He stacked up his record of pleasuring women until he scarcely dared enter a village or tavern for fear an irate husband, brother, or lover would shoot him down like a dog, as plenty threatened to do. Raike, who had never carried a weapon of any kind except a hunting knife to skin game for the pot, would have fared badly in this kind of encounter.

And then, one winter of terrible iron cold, the long, long body of Raike Gaston was found, frozen stiff, in an icy ditch near Osceola. The ditch was actually a seepage tunnel from the levee, holding in check the turbulent Mississippi. So died the long boy of Tennessee—in the open, under the frosty stars.